THE
AQUARIUM TECHNOLOGY HANDBOOK
Fundamentals, Equipment and Practice

TONY JENNO

David & Charles
Newton Abbot   London   North Pomfret (Vt)

British Library Cataloguing in Publication Data

Jenno, A.
The aquarium technology handbook: fundamentals
equipment and practice.——2nd rev. ed.
1. Aquariums
I. Title   II. Jenno, A. Aquarium technology
639.3'4   SF457

ISBN 0-7153-8690-5

Line illustrations adapted by Ethan Danielson

First published as *Aquarium Technology* by Barry Shurlock, 1976
Second, revised edition published by David & Charles, 1985

Typeset by ABM Typographics Limited, Hull
and printed in Great Britain
by Redwood, Burn Limited, Trowbridge, Wilts
for David & Charles (Publishers) Limited
Brunel House   Newton Abbot   Devon

Published in the United States of America
by David & Charles Inc
North Pomfret   Vermont 05053   USA

Contents

For Jill, with gratitude for 25 years of patience, understanding and support

Foreword

The hobby of keeping fish in aquaria has attracted an increasing number of adherents over the past half century and this increase has gathered momentum in recent years. In particular, there have been many advances in the technology which enables life-forms from tropical zones — freshwater and marine — to be kept in good health in an environment which has been artificially created. While it has long been possible to keep many species of exotic fish and to breed from them, great dedication and considerable skill have been required to achieve success. The wide range of equipment now available to assist the aquarist in his endeavours can make this task much easier although dedication and skill still remain requisites of paramount importance and should not be regarded as dispensable in lieu of technology.

Faced with such a plethora of technological aids for better and easier fishkeeping, Tony Jenno has been prompted to write this book which will help the aquarist to understand the function of these pieces of equipment and to exploit them to their greatest advantage.

The field covered is a wide one, ranging from fundamentals to routine practice, but it is dealt with in a step-by-step fashion and in a style which compels comprehension. A work of this kind is much needed and will afford relief to many a frustrated aquarist.

Laurence E. Perkins
Editor, *Aquarist and Pondkeeper*

Introduction

The purpose of this book is to describe the methods, techniques and practices which make the difference between successful and unsuccessful fishkeeping. All fishkeeping depends for its success on the establishment and maintenance of a stable aquatic environment which is suited in all respects to the needs of the particular inhabitants and any special activities which the aquarist wishes them to perform. The environment must usually resemble as closely as possible the natural habitat in which the chosen fish thrives, and this may be achieved either by natural systems or by artificial simulation. If several different types of fish are kept together the collection may or may not be similar to that which would normally occur naturally.

Fishkeeping is basically a fairly simple exercise if the environmental requirements are understood and adhered to. There are, of course, some factors which cannot possibly be reproduced or can only be approximated, but fortunately most aquatic creatures and plants are adaptable. Some natural factors can be reproduced artificially by various pieces of equipment, but the aquarist must understand the function of the equipment and recognise the advantages and disadvantages associated with its use.

There is a natural tendency for beginners in any kind of hobby to automatically put their faith in expensive equipment and feel that with a satisfactory cash investment all problems will be solved and no effort need be made to study the subject in detail. Up to a point this can be true in fishkeeping. For instance, the usual decorative, tropical freshwater aquarium seen in many homes can be maintained easily, with the right equipment and hardy inhabitants, with very little knowledge. But this is fishkeeping at its simplest, and even at this level the application of better methods and practices will bring results.

The basic requirements of good fishkeeping are that the fundamental environmental conditions should be provided by as simple and efficient means as are consistent with proper maintenance. To satisfy these requirements a knowledge of the factors involved is obviously both advantageous and rewarding and can only enhance the enjoyment to be gained from the hobby. This aspect is dealt with in detail in Chapter 1.

Fishkeeping is a very old and well-investigated hobby but unfortunately one in which practical information is badly documented and often not readily available, especially in terms which can be understood by all aquarists. There is an emphasis on information on the fish's physical characteristics, breeding habits and food requirements which, while obviously essential, is not sufficiently balanced by details of their other environmental requirements. Much of the information that we require is passed by word of mouth from one aquarist to another with consequent alterations due to misunderstanding, exaggeration and so on. Many of the old well-used methods are still basically the best, even though they may appear to have been superseded by modern alternatives. On the other hand, with the advent of modern equipment, some of the older methods must now be considered time-consuming and unnecessary, and in the light of modern knowledge some have been proved to be completely wrong. Here again, a knowledgeable aquarist with a good understanding of basic environmental requirements should be able to sort out those methods which, when correctly applied, make all the difference between satisfaction and progress, and a state of mystified slavery.

In the following chapters simple, safe and reliable methods are recommended for various aquatic environments, and the principles behind these practices and the functions of any equipment associated with them are explained. The cost of individual items of equipment should not prove a major drawback to good fishkeeping because the most suitable are not always the most expensive. As with other hobbies, as long as an aquarist thinks a certain gadget is necessary there will always be someone willing to supply it, probably at an exorbitant price!

On the other hand, the aquarist who is determined to buy only the cheapest and most essential equipment will probably be only fairly successful and will miss a lot of the fun and interest. In general, those items which are required should be bought with due consideration of life expectancy and reliability rather than cheapness.

Aquarium keeping compares very well with most other hobbies as far as costs are concerned. The initial outlay can be a fair amount but running expenses are usually very reasonable, although subject, of course, to the capabilities and fancies of the individual. Some aquarists like to offset costs by the sale of fishes bred, or plants grown, but this is usually only economical for the larger fishkeeping enterprise.

Fishkeeping should be a happy involvement, not a labour or a source of constant worry, and the best way to achieve this is to provide the fish with a suitable environment which can be set up and maintained in a simple, straightforward and uncomplicated manner.

1
The Aquatic Environment

The environment in which fish live in captivity is made up of a complicated mixture of various factors — physical, chemical and biological — covering many areas of knowledge. Of these factors usually only the less complex ones are under the direct control of the aquarist, and judicious manipulation of these can often compensate for any inability to adjust in other directions. An unsuitable environment quickly emphasises the difficulties which are inherent in the basic situation of containing a fish in a relatively small volume of water, whereas correct and knowledgeable treatment will assist the fish in adapting to the rather unnatural conditions in which it finds itself.

The fish in the usual aquarium community are many and varied and may come from quite different parts of the world and yet they are expected to live together peacefully and happily. Their individual requirements may vary in the extreme but there are fortunately many basic factors which are common to almost all species.

Fish can be divided into categories and classified in terms of the environmental factors which form the most noticeable differences in their ways of life. For example, a particular species may be described as being freshwater rather than marine, tropical rather than coldwater (ie temperate), livebearing rather than egglaying, and so on. By signposting its environmental and biological characteristics in this way we immediately know roughly what sort of fish it is and broadly what its requirements will be when kept in captivity. The important point to emphasise is that it is essential to establish an environment which is tailored to a particular type of fish or collection of organisms if they are to be encouraged to display or carry out that part of their lives which the aquarist most wishes to study.

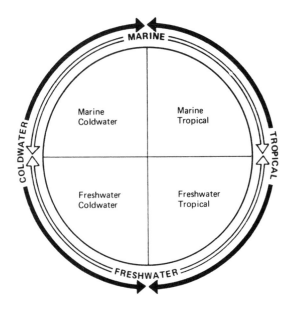

Fig 1 The major types of aquatic environment

Figure 1 illustrates diagrammatically the major types of aquatic environment. The principal factors in each of the four sectors are absolutely fundamental, because almost any fish which is kept under inappropriate conditions will almost invariably die sooner or later. In other words, the correct choice of salinity and temperature is so basic to the fish's well-being that it is vital for its survival. Other environmental factors are not always quite as demanding as this, and in this respect it is often quite possible to keep a particular type of fish for its normal lifespan in conditions which do not suit it at all. For instance, it is well known that fish grow to their full adult size only if enough space is made available to them. There is no reason at all to suppose that a stunted fish is any 'unhappier' or suffers in any way in comparison with its fully-grown counterpart, but it is surely bad fishkeeping to provide insufficient space for a fish to achieve its full expectations.

The usual test for the suitability of an environment is the readiness with which a particular species will reproduce itself in a given set of conditions. As a general rule this would seem to be a fair test, as long as the characteristics of that fish throughout its whole life are taken into account and not merely those which predominate at its normal breeding time. All waters in nature change their characteristics in cycles, usually annually, and the fish's ways change with them. Thus their breeding period is usually influenced by the conditions which successfully promote the growth of their young and not necessarily those which are to their own advantage over a long period of time.

Space

The adult body size of a fish, within the limits of its natural maximum, is largely determined by the space available to it. If this space is restricted by the use of a small container or by overcrowding, then the fish will be stunted. It is not easy to give minimum volumes of water required per fish-inch or similar criteria since the other factors, eg the condition of the available water, affect the result, but if the problem is acknowledged it will be seen that due allowance must be made. An important starting point is to allow as much space as possible by providing an aquarium of adequate size. Aquaria are hardly ever big enough to house anything but small fish, and not even large quantities of those. Of course, if an aquarist only has, say, a 20-gallon (90-litre) aquarium and wishes to keep, for example, Tinfoil Barbs, he will usually do so and eventually come to realise that there is no chance of seeing the fish grow to their full potential. It is difficult for many aquarists to keep in their homes a container with a capacity much larger than 20 gallons (90 litres), and there is no real reason why they should not keep Tinfoil Barbs in an aquarium of this size, but the same argument does not really excuse those who keep goldfish in goldfish bowls.

Space is also important in the relationship between fish or groups of fish whose interests conflict. Territorial fish are good examples. The area of a species' territory depends upon the environmental requirements of that fish and is instinctive. Hence, if two fish of this type are put together in a container with adequate space for only one of them, either continual fighting will result or the weaker fish will be killed or spend its whole life being harassed. Equally, fish which school up will be ·

seen to do this only if the swimming space available is larger than that usually taken up by the school when swimming normally. If the container is of the same size or smaller, then the fish, from their own viewpoint, will be in a school already, but this may not be apparent to the aquarist.

The volume of an aquarium is also an important factor in the stability of any biological balances which may be set up, such as those between fish and aquatic plants. If a container of large volume has good biological conditions and is not overcrowded then changes in balance have a minimal effect and the environment may recover without too much trouble, but in small containers or in overcrowded conditions troubles multiply alarmingly and in bad cases almost any minor difficulty can be enough to ruin the whole aquarium.

Water surface area, which is well known to be an important factor in fish growth and biological balances, will be discussed fully later (page 19) but here it is necessary to question the commonly held view that a large surface area can entirely compensate for lack of space or volume. Water surface area can always be increased effectively by a reasonable amount of surface turbulence caused by an ascending air-stream, but lack of space is not so easily rectified.

The only situations in which small containers are useful are those requiring sterile conditions, eg for spawning egglaying fish, or for isolating single fish or small groups for various reasons, and these arrangements are usually only temporary. There are no real biological disadvantages in using a large container, but there may well be practical reasons such as weight, available space or cost which make it undesirable. However, if aquarists are to progress in this hobby in a satisfactory manner then their permanent aquaria should be as large as possible.

Water

The water in any aquarium is obviously fundamental to the whole exercise of fishkeeping and while it is possible to create almost any kind of environment from whatever water is at hand, it is far better to use water which in its original characteristics is as close as possible to the ideal. Preliminary thought at this stage will save much time later and will minimise the need for complicated methods of maintaining the water in its proper condition.

There are various kinds of easily available water, including tap-waters (these being the most commonly used), natural waters from rain, ponds, streams or the sea, and distilled water from commercial sources (see Table 1). The major characteristics which determine the nature of any water are: salinity, hard-

TABLE 1   COMMONLY AVAILABLE WATERS AND THEIR CHARACTERISTICS

Type	Characteristics	Disadvantages	Method of Use
Mains Tap-water	Hardness and acidity vary with geographical area. Clean, well oxygenated	Contains dissolved chlorine. May carry copper from pipework	Dilute with mature water or allow maturing period
Rain-water	Soft and neutral. Basically clean and well-oxygenated	May be polluted by chemicals from atmosphere or collecting surfaces	Filter if dirty. No maturation needed
Natural Fresh Water	Hardness and acidity vary with geographical area. May contain life	May be polluted by chemicals or organics. May contain diseases or parasites	Examine thoroughly. Stand in darkness 14 days before use
Natural Sea-water	Stable with little geographical variations. Contains life. Usually well-oxygenated	Polluted around coastline. Microscopic life dies quickly to foul water. May contain marine diseases	Collect offshore. Stand in darkness 14 days before use. Aerate thoroughly
Artificial Salt Water	Stable characteristics and proportions when properly made up. Clean and pure immediately	Expensive in quantity. Some trace elements may be missing	Must be thoroughly mixed in correct proportions with good tap-water
Distilled Water	Soft and neutral. Clean and pure	Too pure for biological life when new	Used to mix with other waters as neutraliser

ness, acidity, cleanliness, unwanted inclusions and desired omissions. Sea-water is an obvious example of a water of high salinity. Hard waters are characteristic of chalk and limestone areas, while soft waters occur in regions where rocks such as granite are found. Hard waters contain dissolved minerals and are generally alkaline while soft waters do not and are generally acid.

Tap-water drawn from the mains supply requires a period of time to 'mature' before it can be used in a completely new environment. Not only is it too pure for biological purposes, but it also contains dissolved chlorine which will harm the fish. Water from recently installed supply systems may also contain copper, and this must be avoided at all costs, since even very small concentrations of copper can be lethal to fish and other creatures. Salt is, of course, absent from tap-water and must be added to achieve the required degree of salinity, while hardness and acidity are fixed characteristics of any given water supply area. Information on this last point is generally freely available from the relevant area water authority and should be sought even if the aquarist never intends to modify the water.

If fishkeeping activities can be confined to environments which suit the local water a great deal of trouble will be saved. This is not as limiting as it sounds, as almost all common freshwater aquarium fish live happily in mature tap-water of most kinds, providing that other environmental conditions are correct. Less common fish will, however, often require water of a particular type. Tap-water used in a marine evironment is so altered by the inclusion of the necessary salts that its initial characteristics are of little importance. In all waters hardness and acidity values usually run together, ie a water will be hard and alkaline or soft and acid. This is desirable as it represents the states which occur in nature. Both hardness and acidity can be adjusted by the aquarist by means of chemical additions, and rough measuring methods are readily available (see page 150).

As mentioned above, tap-water should be matured before use in a new environment. When an existing environment similar to the available tap-water requires the immediate addition of water, usually in an emergency, up to a 50 per cent change by volume is often permissible, providing the temperature of the added water is equalised. The minimum maturing period recommended for a completely new environment is one week. During this time the dissolved chlorine will pass into the atmosphere and the water will age to a biological condition which is acceptable to animal and plant life. Stirring by aeration and standing for a further period will improve the water even more, but most of us do not always have much patience and, except in special cases, for instance where a sensitive fish is to be moved from a long established environment into the new one, a week is usually sufficient providing a container with a reasonably large surface area is used. During this period of maturation the water must, of course, be protected from external fouling and other sources of pollution.

Rain-water is probably the purest form of natural water when it starts its journey downwards, but on the way it may pick up all sorts of constituents from the atmosphere and from any surfaces on which it may fall before being collected. In industrial atmospheres all manner of toxic and undesirable products may be collected, and treatment of the water is not always possible by ordinary means. To be safe, this kind of rain-water should not be used. Collecting surfaces for rain-water should be free from pollutants, particularly metallic compounds. Rain-water which is clean and properly collected from a clean, inert surface, will be soft and neutral and ideally suited to many freshwater environments. It will not need a maturing period, and in any event will usually have had one in the collecting container. If it is accessible to birds it should be inspected for fish parasites before use. Planted aquaria and such fish as the popular barbs and tetras usually benefit from the use of good rain-water where the local tap-water is hard and alkaline. However, its use in spawning tanks is not to be recommended as bacteria which attack eggs may be present.

Other natural waters from inland areas or from the sea must be treated with extreme caution as they may contain pollutants in far greater concentration than rain-water, and even if chemically clean may abound in fish parasites and disease spores. There are also many small creatures in natural waters which, while they do no harm at all in an aquarium, are of no benefit either and may develop in sufficient numbers to spoil the character and appearance of the environment. Natural waters are most useful when they normally contain the fish and other organisms with which the aquarist is concerned. However, even in this instance, a natural water should not automatically be considered as the very best for a particular creature. It may well be that in its natural state a creature is able to cope with pollutants which, due to the sheer volume and the movement of the water, are massively diluted. In the much smaller volume of an aquarium container use of such water may build up dangerous concentrations of such pollutants. Even with regard to this argument, however, when aquatic specimens are collected from the wild and their habits and requirements are not known, as much as possible of their natural water should be collected with them and, at least initially, used while accustoming them to life in the artificial environment. Also, if possible, the temperature at the depth at which the specimens normally live should be measured and any other relevant environmental factors should be noted. In this way the aquarist will be able to reproduce the natural situations as closely as possible.

It must be pointed out that if natural waters of any kind are used to set up an aquarium, the continued addition of the same water may or may not be necessary to maintain that environment, depending on the circumstances. In a marine situation, for instance, the continual addition of sea-water to replace evaporation losses would obviously result in an undesirable build-up of salts, as these are not lost to the atmosphere with the water. On the other hand, if hard, alkaline tap-water is added to a soft, acid freshwater environment, the water will tend to become neutral and the benefits of the soft water will be reduced. In soft-water environments any gravel or rockwork present will in any case gradually tend to neutralise the water, or even change it completely over a long period of time, so that 'topping up' with the original soft water is desirable. If, however, the aquarist is specifically setting out to change the character of the water by artificial chemical additions any good available water can be used provided there is an attempt to compensate for its deficiencies and regular tests are run. These procedures, however, can be time-consuming, require experienced operation and are only recommended to confirmed dabblers or those with special situations to cater for.

One last point on the use of natural waters concerns biological filtration, which is fully described later (page 45). Suffice it to say here that mature natural water in good condition is useful in initially setting up a biological filter as it will help to seed the bed with the required bacteria. Also where an old bed is being washed before being used again, mature water will scour away far less of the desired bacteriological population than would fresh tap-water, particularly if the natural water is of the same type as that to which the bed is accustomed.

Distilled water is usually only used to alter conditions in existing environments or to modify unsuitable waters when setting up a new environment. As produced commercially it is of no use to aquatic life as it is chemically and biologically pure. Its addition to any environment tends to neutralise the water by dilution and it is thus useful in arresting extreme degrees of hardness or acidity. In some cases it is used as the basis of artificially constructed waters for specialised purposes, such as spawning environments for difficult fish, but generally it should be considered as a neutraliser and nothing more.

Air

Two air-water interfaces exist in most aquatic environments, namely, that between the water surface and the atmosphere above the aquarium, and that between the water and any air artificially injected into it. All air which comes into contact with the water must be clean and free from pollutants which might either become dissolved in the water or cover the surface and thus prevent the normal interchange processes from taking place. In domestic surroundings, paint fumes, insect sprays, hair lacquers and other household sprays frequently cause trouble simply because they are used in the same room as the aquarium. Pumped air can easily become poisoned if the situation of the pump is such that it draws in pollutants or if it is oil-lubricated. Precautions against these troubles are simple but mandatory; the ability of the water to dissolve substances is so great as to make this a matter of supreme importance. Domestic garden or industrial sprays must not be used where they may be carried into the air and thus into the aquarium. Dust can be kept out effectively by a cover glass, but chemicals must not be allowed into the air of the room where the aquarium is situated.

One of the most important processes which must be controlled in any aquarium is the exchange of carbon dioxide (CO_2) and oxygen (O_2) with the atmosphere. In brief, sufficient levels of oxygen must be maintained to support the fish, while the concentration of CO_2 must be kept low. Figure 2 summarises the major exchange processes which take place.

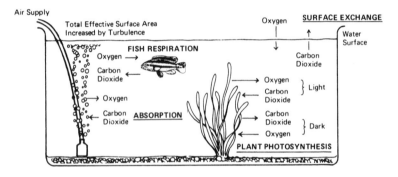

Fig 2 The oxygen–carbon dioxide exchange processes in the aquarium

Although aquatic plants produce oxygen by photosynthesis in bright light during daylight hours, it is only in extreme situations, in what could more properly be called plant aquaria, that this phenomenon is of any significance. The aquatic environment therefore usually relies on its air-water interfaces for the replenishment of oxygen and the expulsion of carbon dioxide by the exchange of these gases between the water and the air. The efficiency of the interface for this purpose will depend on its size, its state of cleanliness, any movement of air across it and the temperatures of the air and the water.

It is often suggested that so many square inches of water surface will support so many inches of fish life in an aquarium. Any recommendations of this kind are presumably arrived at by considering 'average' situations in mixed tanks and contain large safety factors. The aquarist who blindly follows these figures will never realise the full potential of the available water surface. The surface area of the water is automatically increased by turbulence such as that caused by a stream of air bubbles or a filter return system (see Space, page 11); but, of course, this situation exists only while the pumping equipment is switched on and working properly. For this reason it is unwise to crowd an aquarium to the point where such equipment is essential to keep the fish alive, as emergencies occur in even the most reliable systems, and most aquarists' set-ups fall rather short of this. An environment should therefore be planned, whenever possible, to provide an excess of water surface area sufficient to cater for the needs of the inhabitants without artificial assistance. Also, if the inhabitants are not fully mature when installed, allowance should be made to cope adequately with them when they have grown to full size. If this requirement cannot be met or if the likely final population is unknown (eg when fish are collected gradually in a community aquarium), careful observation coupled with experience will be necessary in order to enable full use to be made of the environment, especially if the fish are still growing.

Fish kept in an environment which suffers from oxygen deficiency will lie at the water surface with fins folded, gasping and sucking in atmospheric oxygen. They will not feed or remain active and if this state persists for any appreciable time, they will invariably die.

The absorption of oxygen from air by water is a continuous process which takes place in the surface layer until the water is saturated, ie full of all the oxygen that it can hold in a dissolved state. In a static situation, that oxygen slowly diffuses into the lower levels of the water and is replaced from the surface. It can thus be understood that if the surface layer is continuously changed by circulation the process of oxygen acquisition will be speeded up. Also, the associated stirring action spreads oxygen more easily to all levels in the container. By this means, an otherwise barren volume of water can be completely saturated with oxygen.

In populated aquaria it is essential to ensure that the oxygen is replenished more quickly than the inhabitants use it up, preferably in such a way that even if the circulating equipment is not working the water surface area alone can cope, at least for a reasonable time. Despite this advice many aquarists will, of course, continue to rely heavily on pumping equipment, but they should at least realise the risks they run and should have suitable back-up equipment available for emergencies.

Water does not dissolve a large amount of oxygen by comparison with its volume and this amount decreases with increasing water temperature. Hence, tropical environments are more critical than coldwater ones and, as fish activity generally increases with water temperature, a 'full' tropical environment may require more artificial assistance than an equivalent coldwater habitat. There is one condition, however, which is to be carefully avoided, and this is the supersaturation of the water with oxygen. In this predicament more oxygen is present than the water can dissolve and the excess takes the form of small bubbles suspended in the water. In a static situation these bubbles would rise and break at the surface and the excess would eventually pass to the atmosphere. However, if this state is induced continuously by the injection of pumped air in overlarge quantities, the water surface may not be able to release the bubbles quickly enough. Furthermore, the associated high turbulence may encompass the whole water volume and, by a swirling action, keep much of the excess oxygen away from the surface. Fish which take in excess oxygen are subjected to the same effects as if they were forced to obtain oxygen directly from the air, and suffer accordingly. This situation frequently occurs when aquarists set up their first marine environment and, due to the relative expense of the inhabitants, decide to play safe by providing more air than would ever be needed. There are also sound recommendations from various authorities that marine aquaria need more air than others. The result in some cases is that much damage is caused through this effect.

The detection of excess oxygen due to supersaturation is very simple. Small bubbles readily show up against a dark background in the aquarium. Any piece of black non-toxic material can be used and the air supply should be reduced until the small bubbles disappear, although this may take a little time. Environments with small populations are, in theory, more easily supersaturated than those in which oxygen consumption is high, although this effect is rarely noticeable.

The air-water interface is vitally important for the removal of carbon dioxide given off by fish and other animals in their respiratory processes, and by plants in the dark hours. The passage of carbon dioxide from the water to the air can be artificially influenced in the same way as is oxygen acquisition and it is similarly dependent on the interface area. Since carbon dioxide is more soluble in water than oxygen, it is not so easily removed, a biological excess occuring long before its supersaturation point is reached. Also, a static body of air above the surface does not remove carbon dioxide as quickly as a moving one and this effect is exaggerated by the very low levels of carbon dioxide which are normally found in air. Unfortunately, in a tropical aquarium with artificial heating any continuous air currents would cause appreciable heat losses, but in a coldwater environment a steady flow of air above the aquarium can be used to advantage.

The exchanges of carbon dioxide and oxygen are so similar, although in opposite directions, that they are usually treated as one problem, and it is often not apparent which is responsible for any particular difficulty. However, high levels of carbon dioxide in the water produce the characteristic result of high acidity. As more and more carbon dioxide is dissolved, the acidity of the water increases and may become so high as to be dangerous. This behaviour explains the experience of aquarists whose planted environments apparently alter their acidity values with light intensity, because when the light is strong the photosynthetic action of the plants temporarily reduces the acidity by large-scale absorption of carbon dioxide from the water.

Light

All life on earth exists on food which is directly or indirectly formed from the light energy emitted from the sun. Light is at the bottom of all food chains and is of paramount importance in all natural environments. In artificial aquatic environments, light is usually provided to promote plant growth and to allow the aquarist to see the inhabitants, but the relationship between the applied light and the requirements of the inhabitants is rarely considered, although some interest is being shown now that more people are able to keep anemones and living corals, whose well-being depends on the correct application of light.

Of all the factors involved in the successful maintenance of planted aquaria probably no other single subject has created as much controversy amongst experienced aquarists, or despondency amongst beginners, as the matter of how much and what kind of light should be provided. Lighting arrangements are often blamed for entirely unconnected plant failures (eg the clogging of plant pores by dirty water) and everyone's opinion on the subject seems to vary. Individuals whose planted environments are successful often cannot give any real reason why this is so.

If a small planted aquatic environment, such as a garden fishpond, is studied, it will be seen that there is a critical biological situation at the time in its cycle of existence when plant growth is strongest. At this point the major plant growth will have expanded to fill all of the available light-catching areas and secondary plant species, such as algae and weaker plants, being deprived of the light by the stronger plants, cannot thrive, although they may continue to survive until another part of the natural cycle, when conditions may be more favourable to them.

In an artificially illuminated environment it is not ordinarily possible to reproduce annual or seasonal cycles of light intensity and character, for reasons of equipment complexity. It is therefore usual to try to reproduce only that part of the cycle which best conforms to the aquarist's requirements.

Wherever light falls something living will usually develop. In aquatic environments, algae of various types will appear, either on fixed surfaces or floating free in the water, and, unless some regulating factor is at work, in all illuminated environments all the available light tends to be used up by the algae. In an aquarium this produces the 'pea-soup effect', which is obviously undesirable. Algal growth is generally regulated by plants of a higher order which can absorb or shield out much of the light; by various aquatic animals such as snails and certain fish which eat certain types of algae; and by artificial methods such as filtration (see page 87) which physically remove some types, especially the free-floating kinds. Thus, in a planted aquarium, it should be ensured that the plants selected dominate the algae present and discourage too much new algal growth. Algae should not be eliminated altogether, even if this were possible; they are a very necessary feature of all artificial environments which are meant to be natural rather than sterile. Furthermore, algae are the only readily available plant growth for marine environments.

Where algae live in association with more desirable plants they must be kept in a secondary position. To achieve full growth of the major plants, the light available to them and their population in the environment must be such as to represent that time in the cycle of the wild environment when the plants are at their best.

Figure 3 illustrates the seasonal changes in a natural, planted pond. In winter the pond is in a static condition in which plant growth is either stationary or reduced to dormant root-stocks in the base medium. Temperatures are at their lowest, daylight is dim and does not last long, and any animals present are inactive and do not feed enough to provide any appreciable wastes. When spring comes, daylight and temperature increase, the animals 'wake up' and feed and produce wastes, and a plant-oriented condition develops. Those plants which may have retained their last year's growth will now carry on, but the other plants whose old growth is non-existent or useless remain only as root-stock. These plants need to grow all the way from the bottom to the surface or near it to make the most efficient use of light and this takes some time, especially if the plant food

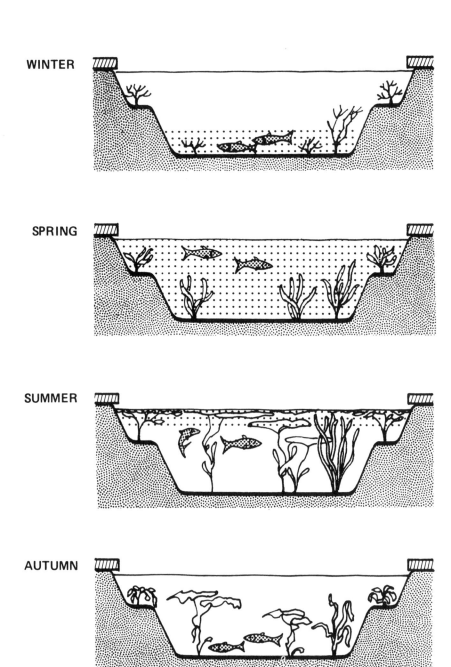

WINTER

SPRING

SUMMER

AUTUMN

Fig 3 The seasonal changes in a planted pond. The dots represent green algae

around the root-stock is poor. In the meantime, in the absence of any regulating influences, algal growth is promoted by the bright spring sunshine and develops quickly, covering all available surfaces and eventually appearing as free-floating forms. The pond then has that familiar 'pea-soup' consistency and appearance. With the coming of late spring and early summer the fish have their breeding period and are very active, producing much waste, while daylight and temperature increase further and finally the rooted plants appear from the deeps in search of light. The algae now go into a decline and a balance is created whereby the major plants fill all the space they can reach and the algae grow strongly only in the remaining spaces. This situation continues through the summer with a decrease in algal growth as the major plants develop further. Throughout this period the water is clear and only surface-fixed algae are noticeable. In the autumn everything starts to rot down or just stops growing, ready for the next year. The whole of this amazing cycle is controlled by seasonal changes in daylight and temperature with only minor variations due to other environmental factors.

It is clear from the example of the fish-pond that we should seek to reproduce and stabilise in freshwater planted environments that summer period of luxurious plant growth coupled with clear water and minimal algal population. The main requirements are plenty of light, both in terms of intensity and duration, high temperatures and sufficient well-fed plant growth initially to ensure domination over the algae. This last point is usually the one which most aquarists neglect. Instead, the tendency is to start with a virtually sterile, gravel base medium, often with plant-disturbing influences such as a sub-gravel filter, and to install only a bare minimum of plants on the assumption that they will grow to fill the container in no time at all. This is a great mistake, because if the environment does not initially have sufficient plant life installed in a suitable feeding base medium, strong algal growth will flourish and dominate the higher plants. The environment will then be a simulation of the spring condition rather than the summer period and may not progress as it does in nature.

Fish do not require absolutely fixed intensities or durations of light, but they do have preferences which presumably reflect the fact that they come from various natural environments and have many characteristics which are strongly influenced by light. The popular range of aquarium freshwater fish can be divided roughly into those which delight in intense light and swim and feed just below the surface and in the middle waters, those which inhabit the bottom and dark corners and are suited to dim lighting, and those which are usually nocturnal. The intensity of light definitely seems to have an effect on the 'happiness' of some of the more sensitive fish. Some cichlids, for instance, will not do at all well unless they can hide in caves or under plant growth away from strong light. If these facilities are not provided the fish may become 'neurotic' and illness or death may follow because they do not feed properly. Generally the tetras, danios and many barbs and similar fish, particularly those which shoal, like or tolerate strong lighting, while cichlids, catfish and the more individual species prefer shady hiding places in bright environments or dim lighting in more open environments. It is surprising how a change of lighting will alter the balance between fish in a community aquarium. For instance, a previously meek, nervous specimen may bully the whole population if the lighting is altered, while a bully used to dim lighting may be virtually driven 'underground' by an increase in intensity. Also, the colour of a fish alters with the strength and type of light falling upon it, so that a particular fish will look at its best only in the right light. Many fish completely change their colours and camouflage patterns with changes of light.

The duration of illumination in artificial situations determines either partially or wholly the length of the fish's day. Within reason this can influence their feeding habits and hence their rate of growth. Certainly the application of regular amounts of light coupled with the usual constant high temperatures tends to keep fish in a perpetual summertime condition, so that they should grow faster and stronger than in nature. This is not necessarily desirable but it is virtually inevitable where all the available light is artificial. Also, fish do not receive the annual cyclic rest periods to which their bodies are adjusted and it could be argued that this may shorten their life-span.

One feature of domestic life which always affects fish which have previously lived in natural surroundings is the sudden switching on and off of artificial lamps in the room in which the aquarium is kept. Nervous fish such as large angels have been known to dive straight into the gravel base or crash against the sides of the tank and suffer severe injuries, if not death, when this happens. Lighting should always be changed gradually or in steps, for instance by switching off the aquarium light, say, fifteen minutes before the room light, and vice versa when switching on. Domestic lamp dimmers are now readily available and are ideal for aquarium use.

Food

Any artificial environment requires the inclusion of food in one form or another and in such a manner as not to spoil its long-term stability. It should be such that it can be absorbed easily and quickly by the inhabitants without any serious effects such as fouling, and of course it must be nutritious and efficient in promoting growth and good health.

Ideally, food should be given as often as the animals will take it. Many creatures, including various fish, are adapted to continuous feeding while others, particularly the predators, feed less often but in larger quantities at one time. Some effort should be made to cater for these requirements, especially in young, growing fish which need to feed continuously, otherwise the loadings on their digestive systems will be excessive. The correct quantity and quality of the food given can be learned only by experience and demands a regular involvement on the part of the aquarist. One of the pitfalls of keeping any kind of livestock is the need to attend to feeding requirements with often inconvenient frequency and regularity. Most of the troubles encountered in artificial environments can be traced back to excessive or incorrect feeding, especially where small containers are used.

There are fundamental differences between the feeding

habits of aquatic and terrestrial life-forms. Terrestrial animals expend large amounts of energy in searching for and obtaining water which fish obviously do not have to do. The water in which they live is a rich fluid of many dissolved salts and gases fairly evenly distributed throughout, so that many valuable chemical substances can be absorbed directly, for example through the fish's gills, without any direct feeding action at all. This is partly the reason why fish can go for long periods without actually ingesting food and not suffer severe damage, although their growth rate may be slowed or stopped and their overall condition may slowly deteriorate. Whether they can do this in an artificial environment will depend on the prevailing conditions.

Fish may be herbivorous (vegetarian) or carnivorous (meat eating), or more likely both, and most species will take a wide variety of foods of both kinds when hungry, but it is surprising how they show preferences for certain items when they are well fed. In natural surroundings each species has its own way of acquiring the food which suits it best but in captivity it is dependent on the offerings of the aquarist. In an enclosed artificial environment the fish theoretically has far better feeding conditions than it ever does in the wild because it does not have to go foraging for its food, or compete seriously for it with other fish, or keep a constant watch for enemies whilst feeding. If its dietary requirements are understood and it is offered the right type and size of food it should come to a better condition than in the wild, assuming that all other environmental conditions are satisfactory. Good feeding helps wild imported fish to settle quickly, especially if they can be given something with which they are already familiar. Young fish are particularly sensitive to feeding arrangements; as an example, aquarists who raise fish in quantity for sale or for the selection of breeding specimens can usually rear them to the size at which they are sold by most aquatic shops within ten to twelve weeks, depending on the species (see page 124).

Details of particular foods, feeding and preparation techniques are dealt with in Chapter 6. It only needs to be noted here that although a great deal of time is wasted by aquarists through inefficient and unnecessary maintenance methods, this is rarely the case with feeding practices. Once a certain feeding technique has been proven, nothing should be too much trouble in putting it into operation, and the regular involvement necessary for the right attitude to feeding cannot be overstressed.

Temperature

Fish are cold-blooded animals and as such have only a limited control over their body temperatures, which vary with the temperatures of the surrounding water. They employ the same processes for the conversion of food into energy and heat as other animals, but any excess heat is quickly dissipated into their surroundings with the result that, for practical purposes, their body temperatures can be said to be equal to that of the water. A fish's functions such as its feeding activity, health and growth, its activity level and the workings of its internal processes, are all affected directly by the temperature of its immediate environment.

Each species tolerates only a relatively narrow temperature range which reflects the prevailing climatic conditions in its natural habitat. Outside this range a further band exists in which the fish can live, but not very well — it easily becomes sick, does not grow properly, and may not reproduce. Beyond these outer limits the fish dies, through the slowing down at low temperatures of its metabolism, or its inability at high temperatures to cope with the additional load on its system coupled with problems caused by the lack of oxygen in the water.

TABLE 2   PREFERRED AND TOLERATED TEMPERATURE RANGES
OF SOME COMMON SPECIES

Species	Preferred	Tolerated
Goldfish (coldwater)	55°F–65°F	35°F–95°F
Guppy	65°F–75°F	40°F–95°F
Angelfish (tropical)	72°F–82°F	60°F–90°F

Table 2 shows the preferred and tolerated temperature ranges of three common species. It should be noticed that this table demonstrates the two major divisions of aquarium fish, namely, tropical and coldwater, reflecting the overwhelming importance of environmental temperature in their lives, but also shows the guppy as an interesting exception which can live in both temperature ranges.

Because of the limitations of available equipment, artificial environments which require heat are usually maintained at some more or less constant value, rather than being allowed to wander over a limited range in daily and seasonal cycles, as in nature. This is particularly true today due to the use of electrical heating methods. In former days, when gas and solid fuel boilers were used to heat fish houses for instance, cycles could be arranged fairly easily and in fact often could not be avoided due to the greater influence of ambient temperature on these systems. This, however, was probably the only advantage of the old methods and it is doubtful whether it was often exploited intentionally. The temperature of the environments in which tropical fish are kept is usually maintained within about 4°F (2°C) of the chosen point. It is possible to obtain thermostats which produce a differential of only 1°F (0.5°C) but this is unnecessary and is certainly of no benefit to the fish.

The selected temperature should be representative of the fish's daytime surroundings in its natural environment during the summer period of its annual cycle. A middle temperature of 76°F (24.5°C) with a differential range from 74°–78°F (23.5°– 25.5°C) is the basic temperature band generally used in tropical fishkeeping. This is based on the long experience of many aquarists as being that best suited to the common community-type environment and a good starting point for tropical fish whose temperature characteristics are unknown. Obviously a few degrees either side of this range will not harm healthy fish as long as there are no rapid changes, but a sudden drop of only 5°F (3°C) can be fatal as a result of shock or the development of disease.

The so-called coldwater group of fish shows several interesting aspects of temperature tolerance. The common goldfish and most of its varieties are unusually adaptable to gradual temperature changes. They are frequently kept in tropical conditions yet also survive winters in iced-over ponds. Some of the fancier varieties tend to favour the warmer ranges but generally the goldfish seems able to succeed in all situations. On the other hand, various wild coldwater fish do not survive in aquaria or shallow ponds because they require colder temperatures than can be provided with normal equipment. The perch is a good example of this and many native marine fish suffer from the same disadvantage. As no suitable refrigerating equipment for aquaria is readily available, these fish cannot be kept very successfully, which is a great pity because, for instance, a perch in good condition in a truly representative environment is probably as attractive as any other freshwater fish.

Once a satisfactory temperature has been arrived at for a certain species this will normally be altered only to induce reproduction or to combat disease. Otherwise temperatures are usually maintained automatically around this fixed value and the fish grow accustomed to a virtually constant temperature. Whether this is bad for them is difficult to say. It would seem that as long as the value is within the normal range of their natural adaptation they should cope, but it is questionable whether an old fish having spent all its life at one temperature could survive a permanent change of say 5°F (3°C) and also whether aquarium-bred fish could cope with the fluctuations encountered in nature. Once fish have become accustomed to life at constant temperatures then it is wise to take every precaution against sudden or permanent changes.

In mixed environments of fish, plants and other aquatic animals the situation may become more difficult unless the inhabitants all live naturally within the same temperature range. Plants do not seem to adapt well to unnatural temperatures and the requirements of many of the more exotic animals are not well known at the moment.

The Nitrogen Cycle

In any enclosed container of mature water, organic material such as fish excreta, uneaten food or dead bodies is automatically converted into mineral form by heterotrophic bacteria. These organisms feed only on organic substances and

TABLE 3   PROGRESS OF THE NITROGEN CYCLE, THE RELATIONSHIP OF VARIOUS CLEANING METHODS AND THEIR APPLICATION

Process	Resulting Products	Relevant Methods	Mode of Operation
Accumulation of dead animal and plant remains, excreta and urine, uneaten food	Organic waste as visible detritus and dissolved organic chemicals	a) siphoning and manual removal b) mechanical filtering with straining materials c) adsorption by activated carbon	Removes large accessible pieces. Removes small pieces to reduce turbidity. Removes dissolved organics
Mineralisation of organic waste by heterotrophic bacteria	Ammonia compounds typical toxic level 0.5mg/litre	a) water changing, completely, or partially b) de-ionising resins c) air-stripping with bubble columns and protein skimmers d) ozonisation by air containing triatomic oxygen	Dilutes toxic concentrations. Absorbs ammonia unsuitable for salt water. Oxidises ammonia by air contact. Skimmer collects scum residue. Ozone contact oxides ammonia kills micro-organisms
Nitrification of ammonia by autotrophic bacteria	Nitrite: typical toxic level 15mg/litre. Nitrate: typical toxic level 150mg/litre	a) biological filtra-tion by sub-gravel filters or external beds b) plant and algal growth	Sufficient inorganic material in aerobic conditions promotes large nitrifying bacteria colony. Absorbs nitrates as food
Nitrification of nitrite and nitrate by both heterotrophic and autotrophic bacteria	Nitrous oxide and nitrogen. Both harmless	Nitrogen cycle completed	

develop quite easily and naturally wherever sufficient food of this kind is available. For practical purposes the result of their activity is the production from waste material of substances such as ammonia, which in sufficient quantities are toxic to fish and other animals. This process of breaking organic matter into simple chemicals is a fundamental part of what is known as the nitrogen cycle (Figure 4 and Table 3) and when the cycle is completed the wastes are eventually converted into nitrogen and nitrous oxide, both of which are harmless to the inhabitants of the environment. Alternatively, the nitrogenous minerals (nitrites and nitrates) are absorbed by plants, and then by some animals, thereby completing the cycle.

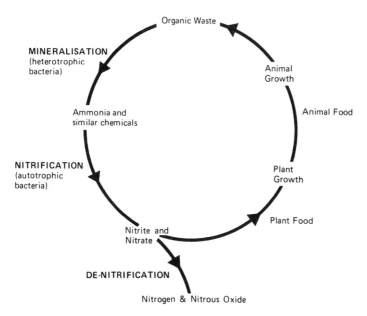

Fig 4 The nitrogen cycle

The problem in completing the nitrogen cycle comes at the second stage where by various means the highly toxic ammonia is converted to the less harmful nitrates and nitrites by autotrophic bacteria, which feed on inorganic substances and use carbon dioxide in the conversion process. Whereas the development of heterotrophic mineralising bacteria depends on the quantity of waste available, nitrifying bacteria cannot develop in large quantities unless sufficient inorganic material of a suitable type (eg rocks, glass, gravel) is present. If the aquarist does not include enough of this material, or some substitute for it, the nitrogen cycle will only be partially completed and the only protection against increasing toxicity in the aquarium will be scrupulous cleanliness and the exclusion of all wastes. This is a lengthy and tedious process which can usually be avoided by careful management.

The third stage of the process, in which nitrates and nitrites are converted to free nitrogen and nitrous oxide, is carried out by both heterotrophic and autotrophic bacteria and is automatic, providing the second stage has been satisfactorily completed. A further requirement for the completion of the cycle is that aerobic (oxygen-rich) conditions should occur wherever the autotrophic bacteria are situated. Anaerobic conditions, familiar to aquarists as black smelly gravel in over-fed, neglected environments, must always be avoided.

There are various methods of completing or substituting for the difficult second stage of the cycle, thereby ensuring continuous purity of the water. Table 4 summarises the methods. The measures adopted depend on the severity of any likely pollution and how much time and effort the aquarist is prepared to spend. The obvious straightforward method is to change a proportion of the water periodically, thus regularly reducing the concentration of toxic ammonia to acceptable levels. This procedure has the disadvantage that otherwise useful mature water is thrown away, chlorine is introduced with new tap-water, and that water changing is hard work. The second remedy, where the environment is suitable, is to grow submerged aquatic plants and/or algae in such quantities that the plants use up mineral salts as food at the same rate as they are produced from organic wastes, thus maintaining the purity of the water. Generally, this system is practical only in habitats in which the fish do not eat the plants.

Further methods of dealing with ammonia utilise various items of specialised equipment, either to complete the nitrogen

TABLE 4   METHODS FOR THE COMPLETION OF THE SECOND STAGE OF THE NITROGEN CYCLE

Method	Disadvantages	Comments
Siphoning and manual removal	Removes only that visible	Useful for removal of large pieces or accumulations
Mechanical filtration (straining)	Removes only materials which water circulation system brings into the filter body. Must be frequently cleaned. Dissolved organics remain	Reduces turbidity where inhabitants dig or are messy. Strong and continuous action possible
Activated carbon	Holds dissolved organics for disposal. When 'full' can suddenly release load back into water. In use must be pre-washed to remove dust and changed often. Adsorbs medicines and other additives	Extremely efficient when properly operated. Can be re-used following steam-pressure cleaning. Removes urine
Water changing	Hard work. Partial changes only give proportionate dilution. Continuous or frequent new water inputs not always beneficial due to chlorine content and temperature matching, and salt depletion in marine environments	The only reliable method for fast action in emergency situations or where a pollutant is synthetic
De-ionising	Removes too many valuable elements from salt water. Subject to fouling by unabsorbed organic substances. Some resins toxic themselves	Expensive. Study of available types essential. Not generally recommended
Air-stripping	May increase pH value by removing weak acids normally present. Foam must be regularly removed from skimmers. Effective only against substances sensitive to surface reaction	Oxygenates water. Bubble columns are decorative. Skimmers are quite bulky, so are best fitted externally
Ozonisation	Ozonised air should not be directly injected as it is harmful to the inhabitants in close contact. Removes trace elements from salt water. Difficult to estimate injection rate. Excess ozone harmful	Best used in conjunction with a protein skimmer for high efficiency. Useful in sterile systems, correct regulation must be achieved

Method	Disadvantages	Comments
Biological filtration	Requires maturation period to achieve full efficiency. Medicines and additives may kill filter bacteria. Clogs up eventually if too much mechanical filtering takes place	Sudden loss of bacteria brings about toxic conditions. The most efficient system except where inhabitants dig or disturb bed. Should be primary method
Plant growth	Requires deep growing bed with plant nutrients	Very decorative. Additional urine removal needed in freshwater
Algal filtration	Uses large trays and intense lighting with complex water circulation system	Impractical in domestic situations

cycle or to make its completion unnecessary by directly removing ammonia from the environment. All types of filters and skimmers fall into this category and are fully discussed in Chapter 4. Their use and reliability depend on available power supplies and the degree of maintenance they require to keep them operating. Many of the gadgets available are little more than complicated substitutes for simpler methods which have been available for a long time but were never fully understood. By intelligent application of simple equipment, some attention to the total population of an environment and proper feeding, it should be possible for the average aquarist to keep a container of water in good biological condition for at least one year without any complex routine procedures. It should be remembered that the simplest method consistent with success will be the most reliable and rewarding.

The best and most convenient method for general use in most types of environment is probably a biological method involving a sub-gravel filter. The filter itself and its action are described later (page 92) but its advantages are considered here (see also Table 4). It requires a minimum of external equipment, no routine maintenance, is inconspicuous and will function satisfactorily for years. The only restrictions on its use are in planted environments, where plant growth is important to the aquarist, and in aquaria containing fish which dig into the gravel. The alternative methods all have advantages in specific situations. Natural methods are a far truer representation of the normal environment because of the inclusion of animals and organisms with which the fish normally associate. In other systems the food which these creatures need might not be readily available. Sterile methods (see page 50) are the best means of ensuring protection against disease or pollution and may be considered useful where a large specimen or a small group of a single species (such as discus) might in any event live in total isolation from other fish.

2
Major Aquarium Systems

If the environmental factors detailed in the previous chapter are
carefully considered it can be seen that all of them are common,
in varying degrees, to all aquatic environments, depending on
the required conditions and the nature of the inhabitants. The
aquarist's objective is to select and manipulate these factors
in order to arrive at a near-perfect solution to a particular
problem.

It is important to realise that, in the long run, the critical
factor which determines the success or failure of any aquarium
project is the degree to which the nitrogen cycle is satisfactorily
completed. Other factors, such as temperature and illumination, are readily adjustable but the method used to complete the
nitrogen cycle is best thought out beforehand to suit the type of
environment planned, since once a particular method is
adopted it is often difficult to change to another without considerable trouble.

As already outlined, there are three basic types of nitrogen
cycle systems which can be used — natural, biological and
sterile, to use current popular terminology. Each system is
described below in some detail, with an account of the various
advantages and disadvantages, the purpose of any specialised
techniques concerned and the equipment used in each case.
There are many instances in which equipment and methods
peculiar to one system are used in another, sometimes benefi-
cially and sometimes not, and a thorough understanding of the
basic systems should help to avoid incorrect selection and
unnecessary duplication.

It is perhaps worth mentioning that the present-day emphasis
on new environmental methods and the use of various
technological innovations has been accelerated by the growth of

interest in marine aquatics and the resulting need for a more careful study of these fish's requirements than was previously undertaken for freshwater fish. The knowledge and understanding acquired, however, provides a useful background for all kinds of fishkeeping and with proper application can benefit everyone.

The Natural System

Environmental systems are said to be natural when they reproduce the wild aquatic environment as closely as possible and use nature's own methods to ensure stability and completion of the nitrogen cycle, without the use of artificial methods and external equipment. The natural system is the successor of the old-fashioned concept of the 'balanced aquarium' and at its best it can approach in many respects this theoretical ideal.

A large container, equipment to provide the required amounts of heat, light and air, and enough water of the correct type in a matured state are necessary if the setting-up of a natural system environment is to be considered (see Figure 5). The main objective, coupled probably with the need to produce a decorative and pleasing aquarium, is to ensure that the gap in

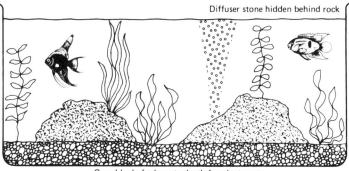

Diffuser stone hidden behind rock

Gravel bed of adequate depth for plant roots

Fig 5 The freshwater natural system. The nitrogen cycle is completed by natural methods involving plant growth and the use of scavengers such as snails and other organisms which are found in the fish's natural habitat. A fertilising medium may be included in the gravel bed to encourage a lush growth of rooted plants. The air-bubble column ensures adequate gaseous exchange and provides natural turbulence

the nitrogen cycle between the automatic stages of mineralisation and denitrification is filled by a suitable nitrifying process so that wastes and other unwanted organic debris are rendered harmless.

For a successful natural system the inhabitants must be fed with extreme care and any dead bodies or large lumps of uneaten food removed as soon as possible so that the nitrogen cycle is run with a fairly constant loading and is not subject to excess mineralisation. The reason for this is that even though every inorganic surface in the environment eventually acquires a population of autotrophic nitrifying bacteria the total area is simply not large enough to provide sufficient bacteria for unusually large rates of nitrification, and so the nitrifying potential of the environment as a whole is low; however, it is able to cope with a reasonably constant medium loading. The acquisition of nitrifying bacteria takes some time and initially a new environment will have virtually no nitrifying potential. The basic objective is to avoid the introduction or build-up in the environment of quantities of organic waste and to install functional inhabitants, plant or animal, whose activities help in the control of this waste and so reduce the work-load on the nitrifying bacteria.

In freshwater aquaria, lush plant growth can be used to absorb mineral salts and should be set in a deepish gravel bed which contains enough plant food to establish the plants initially. If the plant growth is good and aerobic conditions are present in the bed this will provide extra inorganic surfaces for population by autotrophic bacteria, with a consequent increase in the nitrifying potential. It is usually recommended that gravels should be washed, or even boiled, as a safety measure in case any chemical pollution is present but, ideally, when gravel is first used it should be biologically mature with at least a partial population of bacteria. Mulm, debris and so on should also be present to provide immediate plant food. If absolutely clean gravel must be used, it should be 'dirtied' by rubbing with good garden soil (insecticide free) or by leaving it exposed to the weather. If these precautions are taken, plants can root and grow quickly, and subsequently other animals, such as snails or

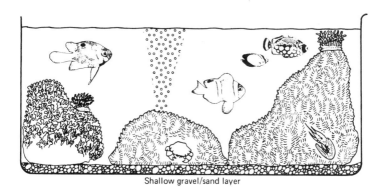

Shallow gravel/sand layer

Fig 6 The marine natural system. Scavengers such as crabs and other crustaceans search out uneaten food, while filter-feeding invertebrates such as living
corals remove organic material from the water. In this way the nitrogen cycle
is completed, provided no heavy loadings occur. The air-bubble column provides natural exchange functions and turbulence

insects, can be introduced. Snails help the process of mineralisation by eating large pieces of organic debris, some of which
they digest and some of which they excrete in a more convenient
form for bacteria to absorb. Other creatures may not be particularly beneficial to the system but if harmless can be included for
decoration or interest.

In marine aquaria (see Figure 6) it is not usual to establish and
propagate a heavy plant growth. It is interesting to note, however, that in the sea many creatures and organisms are found
which effectively perform the same function as the plants in
natural freshwater aquaria. Live coral, tubeworms, sponges
and various other creatures, all known as 'filter feeders', continually circulate the water through their bodies and remove
matter for their own use. A large population of these organisms
effectively removes organic substances from the water and
reduces the rate of mineralisation. This is especially important
in natural marine environments because the nitrifying potential
is usually low compared with that available in freshwater gravel
beds, due to the lack of any appreciable inorganic surface area.
Gravels in natural marine aquaria should be shallow (ideally one
grain deep) since, without the presence of plants or other means
of producing oxygen, anaerobic conditions can easily develop
and ruin the whole environment. Gravels are in fact only of

limited use in natural marine systems since most filter feeding organisms prefer to be situated on rock rather than on loose gravel and some anemones, for example, will move on to the walls of the container if a suitable hard base is not provided. Dead coral material or Westmorland stone (which is geologically similar) with fairly smooth surfaces are satisfactory and anemones will not change position if they are initially sited to their liking. Even with plenty of rock as a base for the filter feeders the nitrifying potential will still be low, so the environment must be kept clean. Fish and other organisms which die must be removed quickly and any rotting organic matter must be scoured from rockwork, dead coral and other material such as shells before installation. Other marine creatures such as crustaceans and starfish are all useful to the nitrogen cycle and are suited to the natural system, provided of course that they are compatible with one another and with the other inhabitants.

It takes some time to build up a suitable population of nitrifying bacteria in both freshwater and marine environments since the autotrophic bacteria develop only after sufficient mineralisation has taken place to ensure enough food for them. There are two basic methods of populating the available surface area: either a small animal population can be kept initially while the population of bacteria is allowed to build up slowly, or a single large animal or a large population of smaller animals which are tolerant of the resulting temporary build-up of toxic materials can be installed immediately, while the nitrifying bacteria develop. This latter method encourages the speedy development of the bacteria due to the resulting high rate of mineralisation, but great care must be taken during the intermediate toxic stage. On balance, the first method, which is slower, is more suitable for use in a natural system, especially a marine one in which the filter feeders would have to be installed after the toxic stage in the second method. Any large, hardy animal, for instance a turtle, can be used in this second method, and would normally be removed afterwards rather than becoming a permanent part of the natural system since its copius wastes would probably overload even the final bacterial population.

A good, easily understood example of a natural system is a

successful goldfish pond, where all the points given above are satisfied and the only regular involvement on the part of the aquarist is to provide food. A thorough study of such a situation will be of benefit to aquarists involved in other types of fish-keeping.

It should be pointed out here that fish parasites and disease organisms can live as easily in a natural system as in their home waters, so care must be taken to exclude them completely. A diverse living population makes medication extremely difficult, since a cure for one organism often poisons another. It is better to remove isolated cases of infection or sickness for treatment elsewhere, and all new additions must be thoroughly and effectively quarantined before inclusion. Where contagious epidemics are encountered, which necessitate treatment of the whole volume of water, plants or filter feeders are probably best removed before treatment as they are sensitive to many of the medicines used. Often an epidemic will ruin a particular environment and the only cure will be to scrap everything and start again after the container has been purified.

Algae in one form or another are inevitable inhabitants of all natural systems. Brown algae, which grow in poorly-lit situations, are not particularly beneficial and usually not encouraged. Green algae, on the other hand, particularly the soft, brightly coloured types, grow in good light in situations devoid of plant life and give the same benefits as the higher plants, although on a lesser scale. Algae are especially useful in marine environments because of the lack of higher plant life. They also form an important part of the diet of many fish. Algae must, however, be kept in check and limited to a useful function only. In freshwater environments, strong algal growth can smother plants, which die as a result of blocked leaf pores and poor light. Similarly, gravels are grown over and become anaerobic and foul.

Small light-dependent organisms called Zooxanthellae are present inside many marine filter feeders and their well-being, and thus that of their host, depends on their living in properly illuminated surroundings. This fact is well illustrated by the observation that in dim lighting the host creatures lose their natural coloration and become pale, often acquiring algal growth, a condition which is a sure sign of ill-health. Light has an important influence in all natural systems because of the inclusion in these environments of light-dependent organisms. (The remarks made on this subject, see page 95, and the methods of application recommended must be particularly noted.)

There are a few techniques commonly used by aquarists in natural systems which help to keep the level of toxic materials below that which the available nitrifying bacteria can deal with. These methods might be considered 'cheating' by some, but anything which improves the inhabitants' way of life is good and as long as the reason for their use is understood and they are not detrimental they must surely be used. In many environments the aquarist periodically changes part of the water to reduce the toxic content. The water added should be mature and similar in character to that which is being replaced. Mechanical filters may also be used, either temporarily or permanently, to remove swirling debris which may never settle as a result of turbulence. Periodic siphoning to remove mulm and large pieces of uneaten food, and the cleaning of the front glass for good visibility, are both often necessary. The use of a column of air bubbles to induce water movement and avoid the effects of thermal stratification also helps to oxygenate the water and in fact to some extent duplicates the action of a protein skimmer in breaking up toxic wastes (see page 54).

The problem of uric acid is one instance in which the marine environment has an advantage over the freshwater one. Freshwater fish excrete large quantities of urine because their bodies have a greater salt content than the surrounding water and to maintain an internal balance they must frequently discharge unwanted substances. With marine fish the flow is in the opposite direction. Although they 'drink' and purify large quantities of sea-water to maintain the internal balance, and also continuously excrete large volumes of liquid, this does not contain much uric acid. For this reason, uric acid is not present in significant concentrations in marine environments and in fact for practical purposes can be considered absent. Activated charcoal filters are often used in freshwater environments to absorb urine.

Oxygenation in natural environments is assisted by photosynthesis in the higher plants and algae in strong light, and by the Zooxanthellae present in filter feeders. Also, some form of air injection by pumping is usually necessary to provide water movement so oxygenation is not a problem unless the environment is overstocked. In nature, marine habitats are often very rich in oxygen because of the swirling currents found around coral reefs and the wave activity at the surface; thus some marine creatures may be more sensitive to oxygen shortage than might be expected. On the other hand, many marine organisms are easily damaged by entrapped air caused by supersaturated conditions (or by handling out of water) so oxygenation must not be overdone and a fine balance must be struck.

The Biological System

In the biologically filtered environment, use is made of the fact that if aerobic conditions exist nitrifying bacteria populate all inorganic surfaces. Normally, as detailed earlier, the available inorganic surface area in any aquarium is insufficient to allow for the development of a really good nitrifying potential. In the biological system this problem is overcome by using a deep gravel bed, with a large total grain surface area, through which the aquarium water is continuously circulated by a sub-gravel filter (see page 92), thereby producing aerobic conditions and exposing as much of the water as possible to bacterial action (see Figure 7). The efficiency of any biological system depends on various criteria and these will now be considered in turn.

The great majority of autotrophic bacteria occur in the top 3in (8mm) of the gravel bed and only a small increase in the population is gained by using a bed deeper than this. It follows, therefore, that a bed of this depth which covers the whole area of the container base will give satisfactory results. The gravel particles used should be of irregular shape so that they have a large surface area, and they should be fairly small, but not so small that the water circulation is impeded. A suitable size

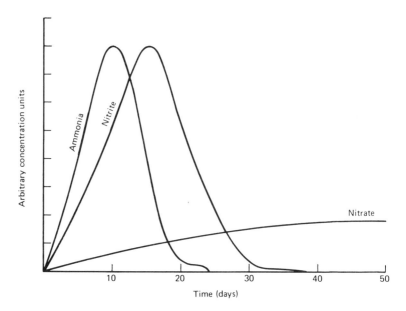

Fig 7 A diagrammatic illustration of the changes in concentration of the various components of the nitrogen cycle during the maturation period of a typical biological system

range is 0.1–0.4in (2–5mm). The depth of the gravel should be uniform over the whole area and the bed should be horizontal so that water flows evenly through it in all regions. Areas without good circulation may develop anaerobic conditions with consequent problems. The circulation rate of the water through the bed should be such that the water is not so rich in oxygen as to be supersaturated but must be fast enough to maintain aerobic conditions. A figure of half a gallon per square foot of bed per minute is usually a good starting point, measured most easily at the air-lift output tube. Care must be taken to ensure that there are no points at the edge of the bed against the container walls where channels of fast flow can develop, thereby bypassing the filter bed. The usual cure for this is to bond the edges of the filter to the walls with an inert adhesive such as silicone rubber.

In setting up a biological system the filter plate is installed on the base of the container and the gravel bed is laid on top. Either mature material or new material 'seeded' with a portion of an old successful bed may be used. If only new material is available the 'turtle' method described on page 42 can be used to advantage, since the fantastic total surface area available makes the nitrifying potential extremely good and the acquisition of bacteria can be that much faster than in a natural system. It is possible to populate a new bed simply by putting a piece of meat or fish into the aquarium and allowing it to rot, but this process would probably take longer than the turtle method as the meat would not be in such a convenient form for bacterial assimilation as would the faeces from a turtle or a larger fish. If rotting meat has to be used it should be ground up for best results.

It must be stressed that while the population of autotrophic bacteria is growing, the environment may become temporarily toxic for creatures which are sensitive to high levels of ammonia and they should therefore not be included until the system is at, or near, its full nitrifying potential. If for some reason such inhabitants are to be included shortly after installation of a biological system the environment must only be stocked lightly until the temporary toxic stage has passed. The level of concentration of ammonia products present can be measured by means of a nitrite test kit (see page 154).

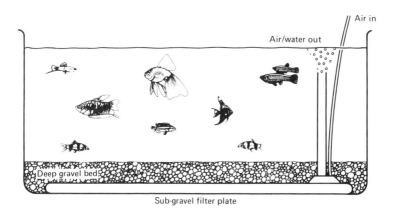

Fig 8 The freshwater biological system. This figure shows an aquarium in which a number of young fish are successfully being reared in a container which would be overpopulated if it were not for the biological system. No ornamental inclusions or plants are present in this specialised environment

Finally, when the environment is at its full nitrifying potential it can be stocked quite heavily and any reasonable amounts
of uneaten food and even the odd small dead fish need not be
removed from the water. Remember that the system is dependent on the circulation of the water through the bed to maintain
aerobic conditions and continuity of the air supply to the sub-
gravel filter is vital. The supply should not be switched off or
lost through breakdown for any length of time and reliable
equipment should be used with an emergency air supply always
available.

In marine environments the biological system has the added
advantage that natural coral sand can be used instead of stone
gravel and this sand helps to maintain the chemical stability of
the salt water. However, some coral sand on sale has a rather
small grain size for efficient circulation and it is worth while
taking the trouble to obtain a larger size if possible.

As well as acting as a biological filter the gravel bed is also an
efficient mechanical filter. Gradually the spaces in the bed fill up
with detritus from the water and this material is also colonised
by bacteria, thereby adding to the nitrifying potential. Clogging
can occur where an excess of detritus is present but in this event
the real problem is usually caused by using gravel with too small

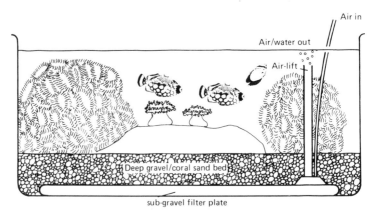

Fig 9 The marine biological system. The nitrifying potential of this environment is so high that some overfeeding, and even dead fish, can be tolerated.
These happenings are not to be encouraged, but they do demonstrate the
system's capacity to cope with common emergencies

a grain size. The design of the filter plate itself and its associated air-lift system also affects efficiency and this is discussed further in Chapter 4. If a bed is washed for any reason after a period of use, this should be done with mature water of the same type as that normally used with the bed, since otherwise most of the bacterial population could be scoured off and lost. Washing removes a lot of the bacteria anyway but reasonable care will leave enough for a good start to be made on reinstallation. When emptying an aquarium, try to keep the water, if in good condition, and use it to wash the gravel. This procedure is particularly useful with marine gravels since these will be thoroughly scoured by fresh tap-water.

Changes in conditions in the environment temporarily affect the efficiency of a biological system but the system usually recovers and carries on as before. Acidity, temperature, fish population and so on all produce temporary changes. Changes in the specific gravity of salt water due to evaporation losses should not be allowed to exceed 0.002 before adding fresh water, otherwise the bacteria will be affected.

The efficiency of this kind of system and its state at any particular time can be tested by measuring the nitrite content of the water with simple equipment (see page 154). A reading which indicates a very low content or none at all means that the environment is 'clean' and that the nitrogen cycle is being completed.

Other filters may be used in conjunction with a biological system but their use is encouraged only when absolutely necessary. For example, in a very dirty situation, where the condition is likely to be permanent, a mechanical filter may alleviate clogging. Also, if any activated charcoal filtration is required it can be carried out in the mechanical filter, thereby having no effect on the bacteria in the bed. Neglected mechanical and carbon filters take on a biological characteristic if left long enough without cleaning, as a result of the eventual population of their surfaces by nitrifying bacteria, but the available areas are not usually large enough to add significantly to the nitrifying potential of the environment.

The biological system is probably the best overall method for general use. Its large nitrifying potential allows the aquarist more time to concentrate on the fish and there is no need for constant surveillance and removal of waste, except in very extreme cases. The system is adaptable to all kinds of environments, is particularly economical and is easy to understand and to use. Marine fishkeeping has definitely benefited from this system as its use has done away with much of the mystique formerly associated with this branch of aquatics. Its serious development is in fact probably a result of the need to simplify the previously complicated methods used in marine fish-keeping.

The biological system is, however, unsatisfactory in environments where a lush plant growth is required. The plants do not seem to be able to tolerate the circulation of water around their roots and it is thought that such highly aerobic conditions may be too rich for them. It can also be argued that plants which feed heavily from their roots suffer from a deficiency of essential salts when the nitrifying action is good. In those cases where environments with sub-gravel filtration and good plant growth have been established, the biological system is probably either inefficient or non-existent for some reason, possibly as a result of low air flow, and the environment is in fact almost functioning as a natural system.

In cases where the animal population burrows into or lives in the gravel bed the system may be unsuccessful because the continual disturbance opens up fast-flow channels which bypass the bed. Eel-like fish may become trapped and die beneath the filter plate if it is not sealed at the edges, or may find their way down the air-lift tubes if the ends do not have a mesh cap or similar device.

The Sterile System

In this system, developed mainly for the keeping of expensive and delicate marine specimens, the only creatures present in the environment are those for whom it is designed. There are no secondary animals or any other biological lifeforms and all supporting functions are carried out by ancillary equipment and the use of stringent cleaning methods. Because urine presents less of a problem this method is more easily applicable to the marine environment but, even then, it is probably only the high cost of some marine specimens which justifies such an extreme approach to the problem of long-term maintenance. The methods are very technical and are totally dependent on the correct application of complex equipment. The system is also artificial both aesthetically and biologically and by its very nature must be maintained in a spotlessly clean condition. Aquarists are advised to consider very carefully their own requirements and other available methods before becoming involved with a system of this kind. It should be noted that the development of successful biological systems has made sterile methods somewhat redundant.

As with the first two systems described, the basic problem is to achieve successful completion of the nitrogen cycle. The equipment which performs this function in this system usually comprises a large mechanical filter, an ozoniser and a protein skimmer (see Figure 10). In addition, an ultraviolet steriliser may be used to prevent disease. All of this equipment is expensive to install and maintain and the aquarist is totally dependent

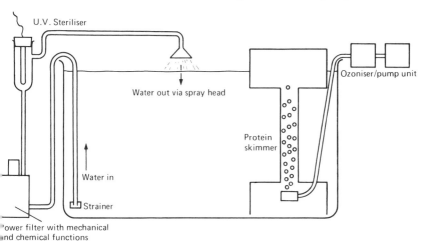

U.V. Steriliser

Water out via spray head

Ozoniser/pump unit

Protein skimmer

Water in

Strainer

Power filter with mechanical and chemical functions

Fig 10 A typical sterile system. The water is continuously filtered and sterilised, and organic matter is oxidised and removed in an ozoniser-protein skimmer unit

on it functioning correctly. Feeding is carried out sparingly and carefully with artificial foods and nothing is put into the aquarium which has a remote chance of causing pollution or disease. The main reasons for taking all this trouble are simply to minimise the risk of losing expensive specimens in imperfect natural environments and also to provide a method which, given the availability of specialised equipment, can be set up quickly for commercial purposes.

The container used should be as large as possible and should have smooth internal surfaces with any inside corners rounded to eliminate crevices which might hold dirt. The only articles put into the environment, other than the inhabitants and the internal equipment, are either ornamental or perform a psychological function for the fish, such as providing hiding places. These corals, rocks, or whatever, must first be cleaned thoroughly both chemically and biologically and this process should be repeated periodically throughout the life of the environment. At such times a larger proportion of the water may also be changed to ensure dilution of any toxic compounds which may not have been removed by the purifying equipment. No small objects or gravels should be included as these would hold dirt and make cleaning more difficult.

One of the reasons for ageing water before installing the inhabitants in natural and biological systems is to ensure a population of bacteria and other organisms from the start. In a sterile system any bacteria, plankton and so on, whether harmful or beneficial, are soon killed by the equipment and so there is no point in supplying mature water for this purpose. On the other hand, the ageing process may remove unwanted constituents such as chlorine and for this reason may be necessary.

When a solution of synthetic salt is being mixed for a sterile marine environment there would seem to be a case for using distilled water, since nothing else is required other than those ingredients supplied in the salt mix. There would then be no organic substances or organisms present initially and this would get the system off to a good start. In a freshwater environment tap-water with the right qualities would be needed, since distilled water without additions would be unsuitable.

Plants and filter feeding organisms cannot be kept in a sterile system since the strong cleaning action present destroys all suitable food and the system is therefore limited to those creatures which can be fed directly by the aquarist. Uneaten food and dead bodies could theoretically be left in if the system were highly efficient but it is better that wastes are removed in case some breakdown of equipment occurs before the rotting substances can be made safe.

The specialised equipment used in this system — ozoniser, protein skimmer and ultraviolet steriliser — can only eliminate pollution of the water if the cleaning action is faster than the rate of regeneration of the pollutant; hence the need for large water throughputs, since a system which is slower will only dilute a problem and may never clear it. This may be the reason why, even with all this complex equipment, periodic partial water changes are still advised and why some trial and error is required in adjusting a system to reach optimum efficiency.

The ozoniser converts oxygen in the air into ozone, an unstable poisonous gas which kills bacteria and also oxidises ammonia. The air supply for the protein skimmer is usually passed through the ozoniser, but the ozone may alternatively be injected via an airstone (see page 85) and thus into direct contact with the water. In this case care should be taken that the fish do not come into direct contact with the ozonised bubbles. Assuming that the correct water turnover rates are achieved, all the water in the environment will frequently come into contact with ozone and will be cleansed of bacteria and some toxic compounds. Figure 11 shows a typical layout of an ozoniser-protein skimmer system. The silica gel column is used to ensure a dry air input to the ozonator to prevent damage to the internal components from any moisture present, with resulting inefficiencies. The silica gel crystals change colour when 'full' of moisture and can then be cleared by baking in a domestic oven. The ozonator must not be contaminated by oil from piston air-pumps, so if these are used preliminary oil filtering must be installed.

The protein skimmer employs the same principal as an ascending column of bubbles from an airstone. When such a

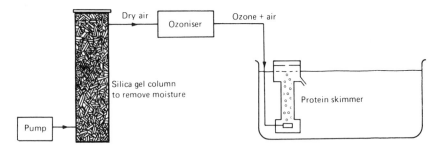

Fig 11 An ozoniser-protein skimmer system in detail

column is passed through a solution of organic water, ie a dirty aquarium, the wastes are deposited as a foam or scum which in a protein skimmer is collected for removal. The skimmer is simply a method of passing the aquarium water continuously through an ascending air-stream and trapping the resulting residue at the top. If supplied with ozonised air it will perform both functions and there will be less residue to dispose of as

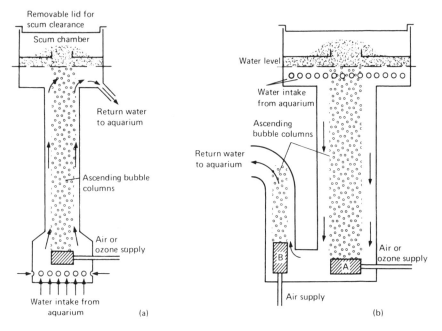

Fig 12 The two basic types of protein skimmer: (a) direct current, and (b) counter current

much will be broken down by the ozone. The two basic types of protein skimmer in use are shown in Figure 12. In the direct-current design the efficiency of the oxidation process is dependent on the available area of the air-water interface (determined by the size of bubbles and their quantity) and the longest possible contact time between the water and the air (maximum distance between diffuser stone and water surface). In the counter-current design the water is made to flow in the opposite direction to the bubble columns from the diffuser. This results in increased contact time and thus more efficient oxidation. The process may tend to oxidise weak acids in fresh water and thus increase the pH value, and may remove trace elements from salt water.

Both the ozoniser and protein skimmer depend for their efficiency on a good supply of pumped air, which in a sterile environment should be filtered before use. On the other hand, with the ultraviolet steriliser it is necessary to pump the water through it and so it is usually used in conjunction with a water pump type of mechanical filter, often called a power filter. The steriliser contains an ultraviolet lamp and the aquarium water is passed through in such a way that the water is irradiated by the lamp. The radiation kills all bacteria, good or bad, which pass through in the water and also various disease organisms. Its efficiency depends on the rate of flow of water through it and on the intensity of the lamp. It has some advantage in that, unlike the ozoniser, it does not inject anything into the environment but only treats water which passes through it external to the aquarium. It can also be used for medicinal reasons in systems other than the sterile type since it does not kill fixed nitrifying bacteria, which do not circulate through it.

Lighting in sterile systems should not encourage the growth of algae (although the cleaning equipment should in any event minimise this), as by the very nature of the system even decorative algae are unwanted.

There is some speculation as to whether fish kept for long periods in sterile environments can return successfully to more natural conditions. It is likely that, having adapted to such clean surroundings, their immunities (some dependent upon internal bacterial colonies) may be degraded such that natural water is harmful to them. On the other hand, certain fish, particularly those which inhabit coral reefs, may survive in captivity only in sterile systems. The reason for this is that the typical reef conditions — high turbulence and strong currents — probably maintain a very pure local environment which can be simulated only by the sterile systems. For these fish all the time and trouble involved in setting up the system will be worth while.

Finally, it is a good rule, when buying expensive specimens, to find out whether they have been kept in a sterile environment and, if so, to consider their chances of survival in a non-sterile system.

3
The Tank and Heating Apparatus

Most aquaria depend almost totally on ancillary equipment in order to maintain a suitable environment for their inhabitants (Figure 13). The misuse of equipment or the use of unreliable devices can therefore have disastrous consequences and so it is essential to consider carefully the quality and ease of use of particular products before buying. Price is not a dependable indicator of reliability and in fact similarly priced articles often show marked differences in quality.

Most aquarium equipment is produced by specialist manufacturers and is generally of a high standard. There are, however, some products, particularly cheap imported ones, which are just not worth having. It should be remembered that gaudy finishes and attractive packaging do not necessarily mean reliable performance or long life. Some items of equipment, for

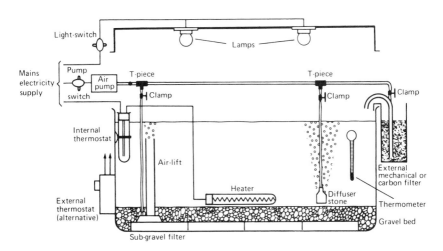

Fig 13 The equipment used in a typical tropical aquarium

instance the aquarium container itself, can be constructed at home with the added advantage of being matched to the aquarist's requirements. Equally, other items can be adjusted, modified or repaired by a handy aquarist who has a basic understanding of the principles and technical considerations involved.

In this and the two following chapters the construction and working principles of examples of the basic types of equipment are discussed and recommendations for safe and simple installation, leading to reliable usage, are given. It should be said here that all pieces of equipment used to maintain a given environment should be complementary. They should not normally duplicate one another's functions and every care should be taken to make sure that the aquarium does not become loaded up with redundant hardware.

The Aquarium Container

The aquarium container must be watertight, strong and rigid enough to take the weight of the water it will hold. It should provide a good view of its contents and should be made of materials which will not deteriorate in use or prove toxic to the inhabitants.

The best commercially-available aquarium container for general use is the all-glass aquarium made from sheets of glass

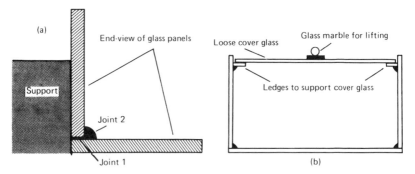

Fig 14 Construction of an all-glass aquarium using silicone rubber sealant: (a) details of Joints 1 and 2 (see text); (b) a view of the completed aquarium, including cover glass and other features secured with silicone rubber sealant

butted together and jointed with silicone rubber sealant (see Figure 14). This method of construction invariably provokes scepticism in the uninitiated, but very large aquaria can be made successfully in this way. The glass must necessarily be thicker than that used in frame aquaria in order to give the same rigidity and to provide sufficient edge surface to bond to the silicone rubber. Suitable thicknesses of glass for typical sizes of container are given below:

	Length	Depth	Width	Glass thickness
Up to	18in	12in	12in	4mm
	36in	15in	12in	6mm
	48in	18in	12in	6mm sides with 10mm base
	72in	24in	24in	10mm

NB Aquarium tanks in the United Kingdom are built in exact inches, whereas glass thickness is completely metricised.

The silicone rubber sealant must not contain fungicide additives and it should preferably be used in an open, well-ventilated space as the fumes are unpleasant. After cleaning all edges of the glass with methylated spirits, joint 1 is made (see Figure 14). The silicone rubber is applied to the base plate and the side pieces are then placed upon it and supported in position for at least two hours. Joint 2 is then made throughout in order to seal all inside corners. A neat finish can be achieved by running a finger along all joints to push the sealant into the corners and to remove any excess. The finished container should be left to air-cure for forty-eight hours. This type of aquarium can be easily made in almost any shape or size, is inert chemically, even with salt water, and does not conduct electricity.

Various other types of aquaria are available but none of them can be strongly recommended, and the only advantages they offer relate to price or decorative appearance. The old-fashioned, metal-framed painted aquarium has now been superseded, and with it the fears of leaks and rusting. Poly-coated aquarium frames are available, and are cheaper than nylon-coated frames, but there is some doubt as to their suitability for marine use. Certainly after a time some of them show a tendency for the coating to split and peel away from the metal beneath, possibly because of the presence of rust on the frames before the coating is applied. Anodised aluminium frames, with either glass or plastic sides and base, are usually of flimsy construction and are comparatively expensive. Stainless steel frames are similar, and sometimes are not in fact rustproof, particularly with salt water. For reasons of economy, both of these last two types seem to be made with as little metal as possible at the expense of rigidity and strength. All-plastic aquaria are widely available, either as a plastic frame with transparent sealed-in sides or as a one-piece moulding. Plastic is not as transparent as glass, particularly in thick sections, and is easily scratched. Algae seem to get into rather than on to it, and it yellows easily with age. A development for the future will probably be the glass-fibre tub with one side of glass, perhaps moulded in, and the whole inner surface made extremely smooth to reduce algal growth.

As already stressed, aquarium containers used for permanent environments should be as large as possible. In the larger sizes, strength and rigidity are critical considerations, especially as the depth of water increases. The weight of water, rocks and gravel is an important factor, particularly if the aquarium is supported on a high stand and a 'sensitive' floor. Domestic installations often suffer from the effects of slammed doors and children jumping on wooden floors. A gallon of water weighs about 10lb and there are 6¼gal per cubic foot, so a container size 36 x 12 x 12in (90 x 30 x 30cm) holds approximately 185lb (85kg) of water, and to this must be added its own weight and the weight of ancillary equipment. Aquarium stands must therefore be strong and rigid, and tall stands should be bolted to the wall to prevent them from tipping or rocking.

The proportions of the container should suit the particular aquatic environment which is being created. For an ornamental aquarium, assuming it is big enough to provide the required volume and surface area, perspective and proportion can be important. The standard shop size of 24in (length) x 12in (width) x 15in (depth) (60 x 30 x 38cm) illustrates the point. Although it is a small aquarium, its dimensions are such that it seems to give the impression of size and space, even when empty. Long and narrow, thin and tall containers may not look so attractive and some effort to acquire a container of pleasing proportions is undoubtedly worth while. Triangular containers fill corners nicely and present a good frontal expanse to the viewer, but their surface area is limited, and so a properly populated triangular aquarium always seems to be short of fish in relation to the size of the front glass. Round and spherical containers give a distorted view of their contents and the latter also have a poor surface-area: volume ratio. For this reason their use, especially as small goldfish bowls, is not recommended. Frequently attempts are made to make aquaria from acid carboys but these are rarely successful, generally due to maintenance problems associated with the narrow neck.

The depth of the aquarium contributes greatly to the total weight and also influences the growth of tall plants. These two points are fairly obvious but there are other more obscure considerations. Where an environment is inhabited by fish which live near the bottom and compete with each other for territories it will be found that in deep water these territories do not extend to the surface but stop at some point in mid-water which corresponds to the requirements of the fish in possession of that particular volume. If the number of fish present is greater than the number of available territories on the bottom, then in a deep aquarium the weaker fish can find some refuge by moving to the upper waters which are not claimed by the strong fish. Thus, in a deep container, fish driven out of possessed territories always have somewhere else to go, whereas if the environment is only one territory deep an expelled fish must blunder into yet another possessed territory and suffer again. A fish which normally lives near the bottom, however, should only be made to live permanently in the upper waters when no other more suitable accommodation is available.

Deep water also gives security and a better appearance to laterally compressed fish such as angels and discus. Tall plants and vertical arrangements can be set up to give a background which suits the fish's camouflage patterns and their way of life. Similarly, in community situations, populations of mixed fish share the environment better if the water is deep enough to enable individuals to inhabit the level at which they naturally live so that they are not crowded together within, say, a depth of 12in (30cm).

Heating Equipment

In tropical aquaria in which the required temperature is above the prevailing ambient temperature, some form of artificial heating must be used together with a control system which maintains the temperature within certain limits. Nowadays, artificial heating is carried out most cleanly and conveniently by electrical methods.

In any installation which involves more than just a few aquaria, heating costs are an important item in the aquarist's budget, so attention to the conservation of heat and proper temperature control is amply repaid. In the home, the aquarium is often situated in, say, a lounge, and in this situation heat losses are not necessarily so important, since they add to the warmth of the room. In fact, a large aquarium can usefully take the chill off an otherwise unheated room.

Heating systems can be classified into three basic types:

1 Those which heat the water directly from inside the container (immersion heating).
2 Those which heat the base of the aquarium from underneath (base heating).
3 Those which heat the air in the room containing the aquarium (space heating).

By far the most popular method makes use of a combination of immersion heater, thermostat and thermometer. This system is easily installed without technical knowledge, providing a few basic points are observed.

The immersion heating system
The combination of components used in this system comprises one or more immersion heaters, a simple thermostatic switch and a thermometer. Each item is simple and reliable and there

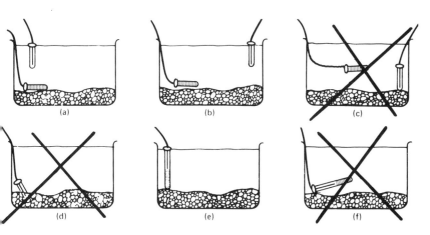

Fig 15 Correct positioning of heating equipment in the aquarium. Unsatisfactory arrangements are crossed through: (a) and (b) thermostat above heater. Two heaters should be used if the tank is very large; (c) thermostat below heater; (d) heater buried in sand; (e) and (f) a combined heater-thermostat with the thermostat section, respectively, above and below the heater (*Courtesy Interpret Ltd*)

has been little alteration in their basic design for many years as they are functionally ideal, although electrical regulations have enforced alterations to their containers (see Appendix).

Immersion heaters consist basically of an electrical heating element contained in a heat-resistant, protective tube. A waterproof cable carries current from the supply, a bung seals the cable into the tube and the air is sucked out of the whole device to create a vacuum by the manufacturers during assembly. These are efficient and difficult to fault. For high wattages, say over 250W, the life of the element may be shortened because of the higher internal working temperature, and substitution by two units of lower power is better.

Heaters should not be moved about while hot and should not be installed in direct contact with the walls or the floor of the container, and are not designed to be buried in the gravel bed (Figure 15). The power of the heater is measured in terms of its wattage and this should be reasonably matched to the volume of water which is to be heated. If the wattage is low the heater may not be capable of the high emergency temperatures sometimes required for disease control or may not be able to cope with the extra demands if the ambient temperature should suddenly drop. On the other hand, a high-powered heater in a small volume causes the thermostat to work that much harder in order to control the temperature properly, and this reduces the life of the thermostat and causes excessive heat loss due to cycling temperatures. Recommended heater wattages are shown in Table 5.

TABLE 5   RECOMMENDED HEATER WATTAGES

Container Dimensions *Length x depth x width*	Recommended Wattage
18 x 12 x 12in	50W
24 x 12 x 12in	75W
30 x 12 x 12in	100W
36 x 12 x 12in	150W
48 x 12 x 12in	200W

These recommendations are for aquaria in warm locations and are only approximate, so that any slight variation from the sizes shown would be adequately catered for by the same value. In cold locations higher values should be used and generally, unless the location is extremely cold, that shown for the next size up is satisfactory. The use of two small heaters instead of one large one has the advantage that there is still some heating capacity if one heater fails.

To control the temperature accurately a bi-metallic thermostat is commonly used (Figure 16). The bi-metallic switch consists of two long strips of different metals, for example steel and brass, fastened together face to face along their length. When a temperature change occurs both metals expand and the composite strip bends as a result of differential expansion. An electrical contact is carried at the end of the bending strip and this meets another on the fixed part of the thermostat body to form a sensitive switch. The bending strip is pre-tensioned by an adjusting screw so that when it is at or below the minimum required temperature the fixed and moving contacts touch and when it is at the maximum temperature required the contacts move apart. The difference between these two temperatures is called the 'differential' of the thermostat and in high quality equipment is only a few degrees.

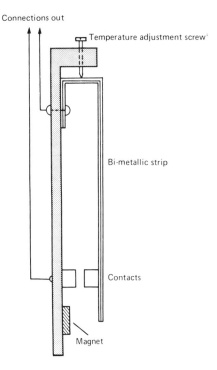

Fig 16 Internal construction of a simple thermostat

Adjustment for the desired temperature is carried out by altering the tension on the bi-metallic strip by means of a precision screw adjuster. A small magnet is fitted next to the contact points so that as the moving contact approaches the fixed one it is snatched quickly into contact and similarly, when trying to move away, it is released suddenly after acquiring a certain tension. This provision reduces arcing at the contact points and thus maintains them in good condition.

Aquarium thermostats are usually designed to fit either inside, immersed in the water, or outside, fitted flush against the glass side so as to sense the water temperature through the glass. They are supplied supposedly set for an approximate temperature but this should not be blindly relied on, and the best results will be achieved if the thermostat is adjusted to the particular requirements of the environment.

Most immersible thermostats are designed to be used in a

vertical position and in any other position the action of gravity on the weight of the bi-metallic strip can upset control.

Externally-fitted thermostats are probably the best for small and medium-sized containers, where the glass sides are not so thick as to impair the thermostat's sensitivity. They are mounted flat and must be in contact with the surface of the glass over their whole face. They are not reliable on patterned or frosted glass which is not flat all over. Any clip used to hold the thermostat on to the aquarium must be non-toxic if it fits over the top lip of the aquarium and this method is useful if the thermostat might need to be removed temporarily for some reason. Clipped-on thermostats are, however, easily dislodged which then means that the heater will be permanently switched on. The use of an adhesive allows greater flexibility of positioning but makes the fixture permanent. There is some advantage in mounting the thermostat near the bottom of the container (but not below the gravel surface) in case the aquarium is only partially filled at any time. External thermostats are safer electrically and can usually carry more current, but they must not be allowed to gather condensation or salt from marine environments and their performance can be affected by the ambient air temperature if this varies greatly. As a result, they must not be fitted in very draughty locations.

There are some important general considerations relating to all types of thermostat. The water level must always be at least three-quarters of the way up the tube of the immersible types and above the top of external types, otherwise they may tend to respond to the air temperature above the water surface rather than to the water temperature itself. Where there is only one aquarium and no spare equipment the thermostat used must be thoroughly reliable. It cannot be repeated often enough that external thermostats must be kept dry and clean.

When a large aquarium or several aquaria using more than one heater are controlled by a single thermostat, the current rating of the thermostat contacts must be selected to avoid overloading and consequent damage. This information is given by the manufacturers and is quoted in amperes. Small thermostats usually have 1A contacts and these carry a maximum practical

load of 200W at normal mains supply voltage. A simple calculation confirms this: watts = amps x volts. Thus, the maximum
permissible load at 240V (mains voltage) and 1A (thermostat
rating) is 240W. Some spare capacity is best allowed for and so
a practical rating of 200W is obtained.

Any loading above the maximum values induces severe
arcing and produces heat inside the thermostat, which shortens
its life and affects its reliability. Small neon indicator lamps
are often fitted and require some understanding. Usually on
separate immersible thermostats the neon is on when the heater
is off and on external types it is on when the heater is on. In combined heater-thermostats of the immersible type, the lamp is on
when the heater is on. This situation is confusing and the
aquarist should ascertain from the maunfacturer's specification
which system applies. Neons in immersed thermostats can be
frightening to nervous fish, especially in the dark.

With careful use a thermostat should last several years. Signs
of deterioration are erratic temperature control, often coupled
with varying differential. If arcing is taking place at the contacts
they may require careful cleaning, although if they are badly
pitted replacement is essential. Neon indicators which flicker
several times at each switch-over indicate that the contacts are
not closing properly.

When the temperature setting is being adjusted to a new
value it is better to make several small steps rather than one big
one, in order to allow the water enough time to respond and
achieve the new temperature before further adjustments are
made. Large, sudden thermostat adjustments can cause untold
trouble when fish are present in the water. External thermostats
can be boxed in if they are likely to be affected by draughts or
interfered with by children or knocked about during house-
keeping. This provision also improves their temperature
relationship with the water.

A thermometer is required to indicate the water temperature.
Great accuracy and a fast response are not needed, so the
immersible spirit-in-glass type is quite adequate, preferably
with a paper scale inside the glass. Immersible mercury-in-glass
types are unnecessarily accurate and more difficult to read

properly in a hurry. A new thermometer should be checked against one of known accuracy before use and rejected if the reading is more than one degree different. Aquarium thermometers have always been calibrated in degrees Fahrenheit and most older aquarists will still use this scale in writing and conversation, but the change to centigrade is now accepted and the aquarist should know how to convert from one scale to the other (Table 6). This is carried out using the following formula:

$$\frac{°C}{5} = \frac{°F - 32}{9}$$

For example, to convert 75°F to centigrade:

Thus $°C = \frac{43}{9} \times 5 = 23.9$, and 75°F = 24°C approximately.

TABLE 6   TEMPERATURE CONVERSION CHART

°C	°F	°C	°F	°C	°F
0	32.0	13	55.4	26	78.8
1	33.8	14	57.2	27	80.6
2	35.6	15	59.0	28	82.4
3	37.4	16	60.8	29	84.2
4	39.2	17	62.6	30	86.0
5	41.0	18	64.4	31	87.8
6	42.8	19	66.2	32	89.6
7	44.6	20	68.0	33	91.4
8	46.4	21	69.8	34	93.2
9	48.2	22	71.6	35	95.0
10	50.0	23	73.4	36	96.8
11	51.8	24	75.2	37	98.6
12	53.6	25	77.0	38	100.4

Where several heaters in separate containers are controlled by one master thermostat the following points must be noted. If all the heater wattages are the same then all the volumes of water heated must be the same and must have similar heat losses, otherwise the temperatures maintained will vary from one container to another. It is very difficult to balance up satisfactorily systems of varying volumes by providing heaters of various wattages and this kind of installation is not really worth while. In any multiple system, should anything happen to the heater in the master tank, the thermostat will sense a drop in temperature and remain switched on. As a result the other tanks will become overheated. The thermostat must, of course, be reliable and have contacts capable of carrying the total load of all the heaters.

Many other variations of heater-thermostat systems are possible. Highly complex circuits can be evolved (see, for example, Figure 17) incorporating extra units to provide for all sorts of emergency situations, but this back-up idea usually fails because in properly installed systems emergencies are rare and the extra thermostats deteriorate from not being used. As a result, they often become contaminated with damp and dirt so that when the emergency eventually arises they do not function properly. Most temperature emergencies in anything other than very small volumes or very cold places develop slowly and should be spotted by a vigilant aquarist early enough to allow faulty equipment to be replaced. Holidays and long weekends away are obvious danger periods, but the chance of trouble is still not enough to outweigh the inconvenience of complex multi-thermostat systems. No circuit of this type can, of course, compensate for power failures, which cause most of the electrical emergencies that are encountered.

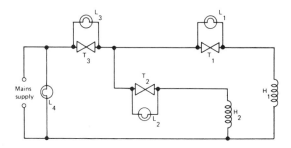

Fig 17 A typical circuit using three thermostats and two heaters to give protection against high and low temperatures

L_1	L_2	L_3
Below 65°F	**Below 75°F**	**Below 85°F**
On-T_1 open-circuited	On-T_2 open-circuited	On-T_3 open-circuited
Off-T_1 switched on	Off-T_2 switched on	Off-T_3 switched on
Above 65°F	**Above 75°F**	**Above 85°F**
On-T_1 switched off	On-T_2 switched off	On-T_3 switched off
Off-T_1 short-circuited	Off-T_2 short-circuited	Off-T_3 short-circuited
or	or	
H_1 open-circuited	H_2 open-circuited	

Heat losses from internally-heated aquaria are a function of the surface area available to radiate and conduct heat away, and not truly a function of the volume. As an example we can consider two containers of equal volume but with different dimensions. Let the first container be a cube with 2-ft sides, that is a volume of 8cu ft, and the second container 16 x 1 x 0.5ft in size, also a volume of 8cu ft. It can be seen that the total surface areas are quite different being 24 and 49sq ft, respectively. Thus, the heat losses from the longer container will be far greater than those from the other. Many aquarists insulate all the surface areas bar the viewing side but it must be remembered that many insulating materials are hygroscopic and so if used in a damp or wet situation will soak up water and lead to unpleasant conditions. As heat rises, it is normally unnecessary to insulate underneath the base of an aquarium unless several are stacked one above the other, when it may be found that a lower aquarium overheats those above.

Base heating systems

Heating from below, through the base of the aquarium, was frequently practised in the past using various forms of power. Gas, electricity, steam pipes, paraffin — all have their uses and methods of application. The main requirement is that the base of the aquarium container should be heat-resistant, yet obviously still waterproof and able to conduct the heat. Slate in quite thick sections was the most popular material while metals were less often used because of contamination problems. Nowadays slate is expensive and hard to obtain, and commercially-built aquaria are certainly not fitted up this way.

There are several inherent disadvantages in base heating. The transfer of heat is impeded by the base of the aquarium and any gravel layer above it. Thermostatic control is easily applicable only to electrical methods, or to gas heating if a little trouble is taken. Insulation around the equipment is required to prevent loss of heat to the surrounding air and the transfer of heat to the container by the source must be slow and even. Direct gas systems and steam piping methods require almost constant experienced hand 'trimming' to achieve steady temperatures and to minimise sudden changes caused by variations in the ambient conditions, and are only reliable if a responsible person is present most of the time, or at least is available quickly. Paraffin, even the so-called 'clean' sort, produces fumes and odours and is only fit for emergency use. Gas fumes can also be troublesome and necessitate draughty conditions for their removal, which increases heat losses.

Base heating is usually used in situations in which an internal heating system might damage fry or creatures such as anemones, or where only minimal heat is required, such as when preventing coldwater environments from freezing. It is not as wasteful as space heating and it can allow a more pleasant atmosphere for the aquarist to work in.

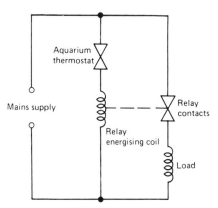

Fig 18 Circuit for using an auxiliary relay to allow the aquarium thermostat to control a heavy electrical load

Electrical methods are the most suitable for a modern base-heating environment and some advantage can be gained over space heating if the aquarist is prepared to take a little trouble over the installation. The application of heat must be slow so that the base and gravel do not become a lot warmer than the water. A normal thermostat situated in a master aquarium, which represents the temperature of all other aquaria, would be capable of adequate control if fitted with an auxiliary relay to carry the large currents expected (Figure 18). When using an auxiliary relay the following should be noted:

1 The current drawn by the relay coil must be within the rating of the thermostat contacts.
2 The relay contacts and their connecting wires must be capable of carrying the maximum current required by the load.
3 The relay must be suitable for mains voltage operation.

Heat sources can be either low-power tubular greenhouse heaters or ducted fan heaters, both arranged to efficiently heat the tanks rather than the general atmosphere. If containers of different shapes and sizes are used, some adjustment will be necessary to account for differing heat losses so that a uniform temperature is obtained. Even so, such a system would be worth while in a large fish house and would be a vast improvement on the hot, humid conditions associated with space heating. It is clear from this brief explanation, however, that the subject deserves far more study and attention than it gets at present, because of its basic advantage of not excessively overheating the air in which the aquarist spends his time.

There are several types of commercial electric base heaters available with thermostatic control which are sold to gardeners for use in propagating plants. These take the form of an enclosed box or tray on which the plant containers sit, and they are quite suitable for use with small individual aquaria. The handy aquarist could make this sort of device and produce something similar. The weight of the complete aquarium would, of course, have to be taken into consideration. In the past, aquaria were often mounted on an insulated box containing one or more light bulbs, which provide a lot of heat, but the bulbs have a short life because they are positioned horizontally. They must also be far enough away from the bottom glass of the container to avoid cracking it through overheating. The method has the advantage that it is easy to construct and use, especially if an extra aquarium is required quickly and proper heating apparatus is not available.

Sterile environments would perhaps benefit from base heating as this would enable the heater to be placed outside the container, and the lack of any base gravel bed in this system would encourage good heat transfer. Also, the very turbulent conditions which are present would counteract any tendency for the lower levels to be warmer than the top. Stratification generally, however, will tend to be reduced even in static water by the heat rising from the whole base area.

Space heating systems
With the advent of cheap and efficient electrical fan heaters for domestic and greenhouse applications there is a trend amongst aquarists to opt for space heating in even quite small fish houses. Fan heaters can provide a clean, fast-acting supply of heat and are readily suitable for thermostatic control. The fan action allows heat to be directed horizontally and has a strong mixing function so that serious stratification does not occur. The heaters are simple to install and do not require complicated maintenance. They can, however, be very expensive to operate if used continuously, and this is their main disadvantage.

A basic principle which governs any comparison of internal and external methods of heating of aquaria is that it is far cheaper to heat the water directly and minimise the heat losses to the surrounding air than it is to heat the air in order to warm the water. Water has a higher heat-holding capacity than air and it cannot therefore release heat as quickly or acquire it so readily. Also, glass is not a good conductor of heat and these two facts together make for inefficiency in space heating systems. Obviously, to pass heat from one place to another the source must be hotter and so the air in a space-heated enclosure with thermostatic control might have to be at, say, 80°F (27°C) for much of the time in order to provide water at a constant temperature of 75°F (24°C). This temperature level is not pleasant for the aquarist and, in fact, cannot be tolerated for any length of time if it is coupled with high humidity. Because of the rate at which such a high air temperature causes heat to be lost to the outside in temperate climates, the whole building needs to be insulated and ventilation is usually minimal. This results in the exclusion of natural air movement and light. Also, aquaria must be covered to counter the high rate of evaporation and artificial lighting must be provided both for the environments and for the aquarist's workspace. All these requirements lead to a fairly complex installation which, even if it can be made reasonably economic, may be unpleasant and even unhealthy to be in, and will after a time inevitably become dank and humid. Thus space heating systems are recommended only if the aquarist can afford the cost of the extra power required, if adequate ventilation is available and some natural light is let into the building.

There are many methods other than the use of fan heaters but all have larger installation costs and require some sort of maintenance, and the general arguments made above apply to all systems. Any domestic or greenhouse heating system is suitable as long as it is capable of maintaining the high air temperatures involved in heating fish houses. Extensions from existing domestic systems are often carried out with advantages of installation cost. Gas fires without proper flues, and paraffin heaters, must not be used, however, because of the dangers of toxic fumes. They also produce a scum or film on any water surface, which is difficult to remove. Boiler systems with steam pipes require experienced manual regulation for good control at all times.

Conclusions

Where individual aquaria are kept in domestic situations it is obvious that the only worthwhile heating system is that using electrical immersion heaters designed for aquarium use. The only exception is the possible use of base heating for sterile environments or fry-raising aquaria. Recommendations are in order, however, for some optimum form of base heating system for use in fish houses and other collections of aquaria.

The amateur aquarist, setting up a fish house for pleasure rather than profit, and requiring economy in running costs, will find the immersion system convenient as it will allow aquaria to be installed one by one, and each aquarium can be a complete individual environment with separate temperature adjustment, insulation and other features. Heaters and thermostats can be bought as they are needed and, in fact, once the building and its electrical supply system are set up there need be no further large single expense.

The advantages of flexibility and individuality in a multiple immersion heater system are gained at the cost of some unavoidable complexity in the electrical wiring system. Each aquarium must have a power point and any other connections such as those between the heaters and any separate thermostats must be catered for. The total current involved in the event of all the heaters being on together, as well as the lights, pumps and other equipment may be considerable and must be properly allowed for. Also, if the aquaria are well-insulated, some means of keeping the room temperature at a low but comfortable level for the aquarist in winter must be provided, either by insulation of the building or by some kind of background heating.

In commercial establishments, where the aquarist is breeding fish in reasonable quantities in fairly crowded environments, many of which contain small fry, the immersion system can have disadvantages, as already mentioned. There is also the problem that where frequent water changing and tank cleaning are carried out the numerous electrical cables involved may be a serious inconvenience, and if their condition is allowed to deteriorate they may become dangerous when water is spilled, as must inevitably happen sooner or later. In this case, base or space heating should be considered, but it must be pointed out that, if profits are required, both of these systems must be fully loaded and used at maximum potential right from the start. A space-heated building only half full will never pay unless the aquarist is producing some valuable rarity which renders all running costs negligible.

Emergencies

It should be assumed that the responsible aquarist will always keep spare heaters and thermostats. If this is not done, and the thermostat has failed and cannot be replaced immediately, the heater can be wired directly into the mains supply and switched on and off manually, following reference to the thermometer reading. This, of course, requires almost continuous close attention.

During power failures only small aquaria or those in very cold surroundings lose heat quickly, and in fact loss of aeration is often more important than temporary loss of heating. A large aquarium can usually withstand a power failure lasting for a few hours without serious results and, if needed, closed bottles of warm water can be put into the aquarium. This practice must not be overdone and, like all manual methods, it must be applied gradually. Low voltage heaters and also small pumps which work from car batteries are available, while some pumps have their own internal batteries.

In fish houses, paraffin heaters are probably the best emergency heat sources, provided every precaution is taken against fumes. An insulated building does not lose heat too quickly if the doors and windows are kept shut, and old newspapers laid on the aquaria provide good temporary insulation, but if paraffin is used, ventilation must be provided and the expense of fuel should not be considered during an emergency. If aquaria are individually insulated it is perhaps worth while to keep a stock of extra pieces of insulation so that the viewing sides can also be insulated if necessary.

4
Air Supplies and Filtration

Air injected into aquatic environments has three basic functions: (a) to provide oxygen, remove carbon dioxide and break down toxic wastes by its contact with the water; (b) to provide motive power for the circulation of water by air-lift mechanisms; and (c) to induce water movement and general turbulence. Ascending air-streams also provide an attractive feature. A typical installation is shown in Figure 19.

It is well known that atmospheric pressure (average 14.7lb per sq in) will support a water column 34ft high. From this fact

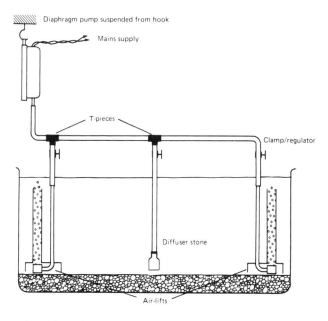

Fig 19 A typical air-supply system. The diaphragm pump should be positioned at least 6in above the water surface. All piping should be kept as short as possible to encourage the build up of a back pressure

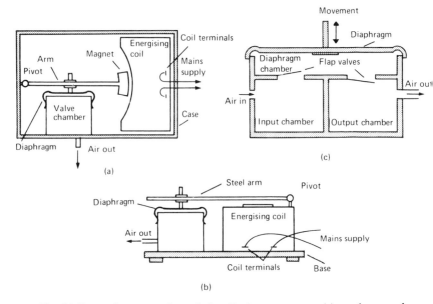

Fig 20 Internal construction of the diaphragm pump: (a) modern, and (b) older design; (c) the valve chamber

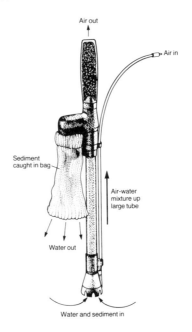

Fig 21 An air-operated water strainer and sediment remover, a useful cleaning tool

it can be calculated that a column only 1in high is supported by a pressure of only 0.036lb per sq in. Therefore, to force air to a depth of even 24in, which is deeper than most ordinary aquaria, only a very small pressure is required. This conclusion is of great importance to aquarists for it allows the use of extremely simple air pumps.

The most popular type of small pump uses the vibrating diaphragm mechanism which pushes air through a simple automatic valve system and is operated by a magnetic coil fed directly from the mains supply (Figure 20). These pumps are cheap, efficient, easy to repair and maintain, and the larger models supply considerable amounts of air and are quite adequate for multiple installations or for driving air-powered cleaning tools (Figure 21). The most frequently encountered problem with this type is noise and vibration, generated by the diaphragm moving quite powerfully, usually at fifty impulses per second in sympathy with the frequency of the mains supply. Recent models have been improved by positioning the diaphragm-actuating lever so that it is not in contact with the coil (in older models the coil was also the mounting for the lever) but though noise problems have thereby been minimised they have not always been eliminated. Since, however, there is no comparable alternative to this type of pump, the aquarist is recommended to try to understand the problems and then to eliminate their effects, which in all but the worse cases can easily be achieved.

Vibrator pumps are best suspended from a strong hook so that they do not come into contact with anything which might amplify the vibration. Many pumps are provided with a hole for this purpose, moulded into a rubber baseplate, but in use the rubber often splits. If the pump is placed upon a smooth surface it may 'walk' about under the influence of its internal vibrations and some have been known to creep off shelves in this way! Pumps must not be silenced by being shut up in boxes or very small cupboards as they tend to overheat without adequate air circulation. If they are mounted level with, or below, the surface of the water in an aquarium, and particularly if stood on the floor below it, they must have a non-return valve fitted in the supply line. If this is not done, then when they are switched off (or if a power failure occurs) the aquarium may empty via the pump due to a siphon action through an open valve. To make matters worse, the pump subsequently floods internally and if switched on again, as happens automatically at the end of a power failure, will be severely damaged. The non-return valve prevents this happening and if this is not fitted the pump must be installed at least a foot above the water level.

Maintenance of vibrator pumps usually involves only the replacement of burst diaphragms and the periodic cleaning of the small flap valves if the pump is used in a dusty atmosphere without an input air filter. Parts are generally readily available and the practical aquarist should be able to carry out all repairs. One word of caution: in some older models the rubber base is only popped on or held by a rubber lip. The base is easily removed while the pump is working and in many cases the mains terminals are immediately accessible and often are not insulated. It is thus very easy to receive an electric shock so the pump must not be switched on with the base removed unless extreme caution is exercised.

To test the efficiency of a vibrator pump it should be opened so that the diaphragm is visible and a length of air tubing, say two feet long, should be fitted to the outlet pipe. If the pump is now switched on (remembering the warning in the previous paragraph) and the tube pinched shut near the pump body, the diaphragm should rise up considerably under the influence of the back pressure created internally by the trapped air. The rising action of the diaphragm shows that the inlet valve is in good condition. If the pipe is now released and pinched again at the end farthest away from the pump, the diaphragm should rise again, but this time it is indicating the condition of the out-let valve. If the pump is now closed up it should be virtually silent when the outlet pipe is covered to simulate its normal operating condition, and if the pump is turned upside down or rotated in any manner it should be equally quiet. Any loud rattles from inside indicate a burst diaphragm, faulty adjust-ment or incorrect initial assembly.

Some aquarists like to switch their pumps on and off by

means of the thermostat, presumably for decorative reasons as there is no other advantage, but this is not recommended. First, injected air is needed continuously, especially in the case of sub-gravel filtration where aerobic conditions must always be maintained. Secondly, because of the influence of the coil in the pump, a heavy electrical spark is produced at the thermostat points at the instant of switching, which will damage the thermostat unless it has sufficiently large contacts. For those determined to continue this practice, a capacitor can be fitted across the points to minimise the arcing, but it has the disadvantage that the pump may still vibrate lightly while apparently switched off by the thermostat and in this situation it is likely to siphon back as already described above. Thirdly, with periodic operation the fish will not experience constant environmental conditions, the influence of injected air being spread over so many factors that artificial changes may cause difficulties. Some aquarists switch off the pump at night and this too is disadvantageous for the same reason. In planted aquaria, night-time is just when the air supply is needed most because day-time photosynthetic processes have stopped and the plants themselves are consuming oxygen.

The efficiency of the vibrator pump is highest when a back pressure exists on the diaphragm and this is achieved by having piping systems as short as possible and airtight. The piping itself should be of the minimum possible diameter and air filtering should be carried out before the air enters the pump in order to protect its valves. The pump itself will not contribute anything which can pollute the air supply.

Larger pumps are available which employ pistons to produce pressurised air, again through an automatic valve system, the whole arrangement being driven by an electromagnetic coil supplied from the mains (Figure 22). These pumps are now-adays considered almost redundant, but where the utmost reliability is required they are still used as they do not have consumable diaphragms and their valves are not so subject to clogging. They are, however, more inconvenient to use as they require frequent lubrication, tend to contaminate the air supply with oil and require a more complex piping system. The rotating

Fig 22 A piston-type air pump for aquarium use *(Courtesy Medcalf Bros)*

component which drives the piston has a very low torque or turning force and so the pump can easily be stopped by any small back pressure in either piston. The pump must work at all times almost as though it were pumping straight into the atmosphere, and any excess air produced and not used by appliances must be bled away to the atmosphere (Figure 23).

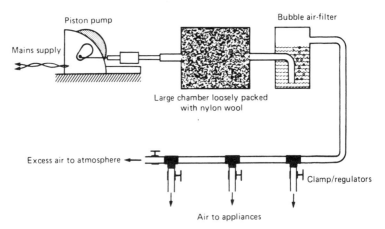

Fig 23 A typical air-supply system with a piston air pump. The pump should be mounted at least 12in above the water surface and should always be run at high speed, any slowdown indicating a blockage or back-pressure build-up, which should be dealt with either by clearance or by venting excess pressure to the atmosphere. If the system incorporates an ozoniser, the water filter should be replaced with a silica gel column

This makes for constant attention. Air filters may be needed to exclude the pump's oil from the aquarium water, and large air reservoirs are advisable to smooth out the effects of the pulsations of the pistons. The whole piping system should, if possible, be constructed in large-bore pipe in order to reduce back pressure, and will generally be more expensive and more complex to install than the equivalent system for a vibrator pump. However, it must be said that any good piston pump is usually quieter and, if properly fitted up, can produce more air than a single, small vibrator.

All air systems must be balanced so that the pumped air is not lost through the channel of least resistance. Thus all appliances must be fitted with a regulator of some kind and these should be balanced when everything is running normally. For example, in the installation shown in Figure 19 each air-lift may use as much as six times more air than the diffuser stone. The resistance to air-flow present in the stone will tend to make all available air-flow through the air-lifts, so the regulators must be carefully adjusted more or less simultaneously to balance the system. Any change made in the air consumption of one appliance may affect at least some of the others and so balancing may be needed whenever a change in demand takes place. Long-term changes, such as the gradual clogging up of diffuser stones, may necessitate compensating adjustments.

For large fish houses, aquarium shops and so on an industrial type of air compressor is often used, fitted with a large reservoir and controlled by a pressure switch to maintain a steady working pressure in the reservoir. Operation of the compressor motor is then intermittent but the supply taken from the reservoir is continuous. By keeping the pressure in the reservoir at, say, 10lb per sq in, pulsations from the pump section are eliminated and some reserve is provided for short-lived emergencies. In terms of the consumption of electricity, intermittent pump operation proves to be more economical than releasing excess air to the atmosphere from a unit which runs continuously. To complete the supply system (Figure 24) the compressor may need input and output air filters, depending on the type, and a safety blow-off valve (set higher than the

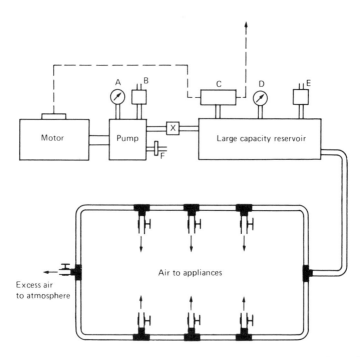

Fig 24 An air-supply system using a compressor. A proper unit designed for aquarium use should not produce any oil or other contaminant in the output pipe of the compressor, but if in doubt fit a filtering system at the point marked X. The unit should be mounted above the highest water level and will require firm support. The supply line and ring main can be assembled from 1½in plastic piping with air-tight couplings. A: pump output pressure gauge; B: safety blow-off valve; C: pressure switch for controlling pump motor; D: reservoir pressure gauge; E: reservoir safety blow-off valve; F: input air filter

reservoir pressure) should be fitted to cover any failure of the pressure switch. The regulators fitted to the aquarium appliances should ideally be more reliable than the simple clamps normally used, since, if one of these should fall off, the appliance concerned might receive a very high air input which could create problems in the environment through excess turbulence or supersaturation. Most compressors are fairly noisy when operating and are best installed in a remote location, the air supply being fed through a large-bore ring distribution system. Balancing of individual appliances may be less important because of the air reserve in the reservoir.

The simplest air-operated appliance used in aquaria is the diffuser stone. This is a block of sintered material which is porous and breaks the air-stream up into a multitude of extremely small bubbles, so that the effect of the air column on the environment is increased by the larger total surface area of so many small bubbles. Good diffusers are trouble free and last for many years. When blocked they can usually be cleared by holding under hot running water or by boiling.

The basis of all air-operated appliances such as filters is the use of the air-lift principle (see Figure 25). If the unconnected air-lift assembly is placed inside the aquarium the water inside the pipe automatically levels with that outside. When air is then introduced at the base of the pipe, bubbles form and an air-water mixture is produced which is less dense than the water alone and therefore rises up the pipe. Provided the air supply is

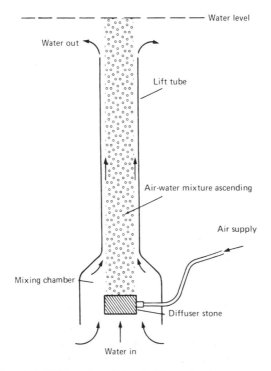

Fig 25 Function of the air-life mechanism

maintained, this mixture leaves the pipe at the top in a continuous process and water is replaced naturally from below. Thus a circulation is set up through the lift pipe and if one end is in the aquarium and the other end in, say, an outside filter, water will be moved from one to the other. The efficiency of an air-lift is best when at least 70 per cent of its total lifting distance is below the aquarium water surface level, and when the injected air bubbles are as small as possible. If the injected air supply is increased to improve the water-flow, a point will be reached at which it will be necessary to increase the internal diameter of the lift tube in order to allow the larger flow to pass through. If this is not done the air will not mix properly with the water and the rate of circulation will not increase.

Emergency air supplies can be generated by battery-operated pumps or by a temporary reservoir such as a large clean plastic bottle or an inflated car inner tube. For multiple installations, which use more air, a gasometer-type system can be built with some time and trouble, although this is a rather large, permanent installation which might only be used very occasionally (Figure 26). The gasometer is made from an airtight container such as an oil drum which has been thoroughly cleaned internally. The bottom end is completely open and the drum is suspended over a water-filled hole of its own depth. The air trapped is forced out through a smaller hole in the top as the drum is gradually forced down into the water. Some sort of guiding framework is needed to keep the drum vertical and some means must be provided to lift it out of the hole again when all the air has been used. The pressure produced at the outlet depends on the rate of descent of the drum and will influence the length of time for which the supply lasts. The outlet pressure should therefore be only slightly in excess of that required. If the rate of descent is very high the air inside the drum may become so pressurised that it breaks the water seal and leaks to the atmosphere. The trick is to weight the drum just sufficiently so that it descends into the hole at a rate which just provides enough air to run the required appliances. Repositioning of the drum at the start position is easier if a large hole can be temporarily opened in the top to admit air quickly. This

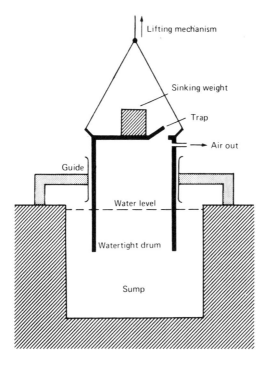

Fig 26 A homemade gasometer-type air compressor. The trap allows fast entry of air while lifting *(Acknowledgement M. Reynolds)*

system is admittedly rather unorthodox and troublesome to install, but if correctly used it can run a fair number of appliances with only daily recharging and it does demonstrate what a little thought and enterprise can achieve.

Filters

Filters for aquaria come in all sorts of shapes, types and sizes, but they all perform the same basic function, and that is to circulate the water through some form of straining or cleansing medium at such a rate that the water is kept clean and sweet. There are various categories into which filters can be grouped, such as 'inside', 'outside' and 'sub-gravel', but the situation of the filter is not nearly as important as the way in which it operates.

Mechanical filters remove unwanted materials from the water

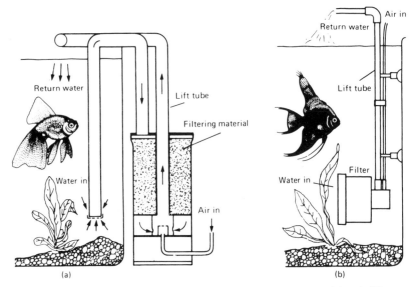

Fig 27 (a) External, and (b) internal mechanical filters operated by air-lifts
(*Courtesy Hillside Aquatics*)

by straining and/or the use of an absorbent material. Examples
are shown in Figure 27. They are usually made in the form of a
box to hold the filter material and may be fitted inside or outside
the aquarium. Most mechanical filters are operated by an air-lift
but some large ones, commonly called power filters, are operated by rotating water pumps. The most important characteristics of any mechanical filter are its capacity for holding cleaning
materials and its circulation rate. A common fault among
aquarists is to buy only the cheapest small air pump and then to
find that the filter is apparently useless because there is not
enough air available to make it operate properly. As can be seen
from the earliest description of air-lift principles, good water
circulation requires a good air supply and wide-bore pipes.

All but the smallest mechanical filters are fitted outside the
aquarium, either suspended from it or mounted close by, and
these must ideally be arranged so that the water level in the
filter, when the filtering medium is submerged, is level with the
water surface in the aquarium. A siphon is then fitted to maintain this condition automatically. Water can either be pumped
from the aquarium to the filter, or vice versa, by the air-lift and

the automatic siphon completes the circuit by continuously levelling the two surfaces. All that remains then is to arrange that the water passes through the filtering medium during its passage through the filter. The air-lift should preferably operate so that water is moved from the filter to the aquarium rather than the other way around, in case the siphon should stop, in which event the filter box will flood, emptying the aquarium. If the water moves from the filter to the aquarium only the filter will empty and its contents will run harmlessly into the aquarium.

The filtering materials commonly used for straining include gravel, wools of various kinds and sponges. Gravel is a good coarse filter but will not remove the smallest particles unless used in very deep layers. It is heavy and difficult to remove for cleaning without dismantling the filter. Nylon wool is a very useful material if packed into the filter correctly. It should fill all spaces and corners so that it is not bypassed by the water current, but must not be squeezed in so tightly that the circulation rate is impeded. Glass-fibre materials should never be used in filters as they produce small sharp splinters which enter the gills of fish and cause serious problems. Sponge material (polyfoam etc) is useful because it can be cut to fit the filter box exactly and can be removed, washed and reused many times. Like nylon wool it must not be so dense that it impedes circulation. Whichever material is used it should be cleaned before it becomes absolutely clogged up or the efficiency of the filter will decrease.

Commercial filters seldom have the capacity to cope with very large aquaria and aquarists are often better advised to build their own from a small aquarium or other similar container (Figure 28). It should be pointed out that a large mechanical filter which is left uncleaned may eventually take on a biological action if conditions are right for its population by nitrifying bacteria, and if its total bed surface area is big enough it can perform a useful service in this mode.

Activated charcoal (or carbon) is commonly used in mechanical filters to adsorb unwanted chemical compounds such as urine in freshwater environments. In addition, it may also

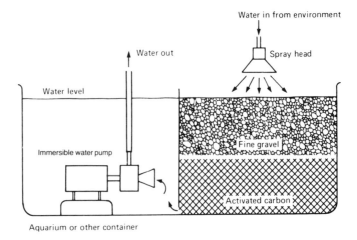

Fig 28 An efficient high-capacity mechanical and chemical filter. The water in the filter should be at the same level as that in the aquarium, so that if the pump stops the aquarium will not empty through the filter input syphon. If the filter is ever used in a lower position, the pump output flow must obviously be greater than the syphon input flow, but the difference must never be so great that the pump can empty the filter, as the pump will be damaged if operated out of water

remove many useful ingredients and in particular it will be found that the filter must be turned off whenever medicines are added. The life of the charcoal filter is determined by how soon its adsorbent capacity is used up and this can be tested by putting a few drops of methylene blue into the filter box. The dye colour will disappear if the filter is still efficient. Charcoal will of course also act as a mechanical filter and, if left uncleaned, also acquire a nitrifying potential. Since it is a very light material, easily moved by the water current, it is useful to sandwich the charcoal between two gravel or wool layers, or to waterlog it before use, thereby reducing the chances of its being swept into the aquarium. A large mechanical filter with gravel and charcoal as its media can be maintained in two ways. Either it can be cleaned frequently and the charcoal replaced when fully loaded so that it performs its mechanical and chemical functions at top efficiency, or it can be left dirty and allowed to acquire a population of nitrifying bacteria, thus replacing the failing chemical action by an improving biological function. The last argument, however, only holds good if the surface area is large enough and if aerobic conditions are maintained in the filter.

A further system of some interest is that in which an aquarium populated by ancillary animals, such as snails and Daphnia (freshwater), or filter feeders (salt-water), can be used to clean the water of another aquarium containing fish which would not tolerate the presence of these animals if they were kept all together. Water is circulated between the two aquaria and the system is, in fact, a complete natural aquarium in two parts (see Figure 29). This method is worthy of more serious study than it has so far generally received, as there are many advantages in its use. Medications which are necessary at times for the fish but which are harmful to other creatures can be isolated from the ancillary aquarium by temporarily stopping circulation and compensating with other methods of filtration. If the ancillary creatures are also food animals (eg Daphnia) for the primary inhabitants they can be cultured in this system and the excess population transferred to the main container when available. Similarly, fish which do not tolerate plants in their environment can nevertheless enjoy the benefits of water from a planted aquarium. Many other advantages result from this system, and of course, with good usage, one ancillary environment may well support more than one primary environment.

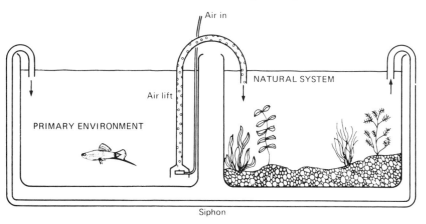

Fig 29 Layout for the use of a natural system as a filter. Circulation is completed automatically with a simple syphon

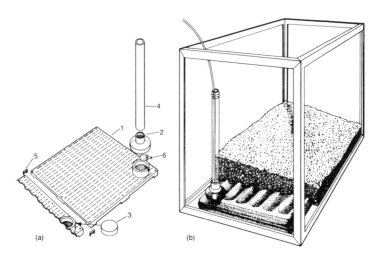

(a) (b)

Fig 30 The sub-gravel filter. An air-lift draws water from beneath the filter plate, which is replaced by water from above. A filter bed (of gravel) is thereby provided with a steady circulation of oxygenated water, which facilitates the removal of toxic substances by aerobic bacteria. (a) An exploded diagram, showing how two or more filter plates can be joined and operated by one air-lift: 1: filter plate; 2: mixing chamber; 3: blanking plug; 4: lift tube; 5: joining clip; 6: diffuser stone *(Courtesy North West Plastics)*; (b) a sub-gravel filter in position (gravel cut away for illustration) *(Courtesy Algarde Plastics)*

The principles of biological filtration have already been explained in Chapter 2, but some consideration of the construction and installation of sub-gravel filters (Figure 30) is worth while. At present these are still being developed and this is one field in which the practical aquarist can often improve on commercial products and, indeed, is even obliged to in many cases because filter plates just cannot be bought ready-made to fit every size and shape of aquarium container. Ideally the filter plate should cover the whole base area and should not allow water to flow past its edges and bypass the bed. It should have an efficient air-lift mechanism which will circulate water evenly over the whole bed area and the plate perforations should be such that gravel, mulm and so on are not drawn through to lie beneath the filter plate and thus impede circulation. The plate must be rigidly constructed so as to take the weight of the gravel bed and any other heavy material above, such as decorative rocks, without sagging, and the junction between the air-lift mechanism and the filter plate must be sound. For added efficiency, the air-lift tube should preferably include space for a diffuser stone.

Materials available to the home constructor are corrugated plastic sheeting, used normally for roofing, and small-bore plastic piping in various sizes as used in domestic waste water systems. Both must be made in non-toxic materials and plastics should be tested before use, especially when they are to be used in marine environments. All cuts, holes and slots should be made smooth to eliminate small particles which could harm fish, and perforations in corrugated sheet should be in the troughs of the corrugations. Non-toxic joints can be made with silicone rubber sealant but tests should be made to see that it adheres properly to the particular material used.

To achieve the most even circulation of water through the whole bed area it would be best if the air-lift were situated in the centre of a circular plate; but as aquaria are usually anything but circular and a central air-lift is not very convenient there is inevitably some loss of performance for this reason. However, this loss can be minimised if the other important points are attended to and enough air is provided.

The main physical advantage of the sub-gravel filter over other types is that it is hidden inside the environment and does not detract from the overall appearance of the aquarium. Compared with externally mounted filters it allows rows of aquaria to be fitted up tightly side by side for economy of space. Its main disadvantages are that it is not easily accessible should anything go wrong and its use demands a deep gravel bed which can spoil the look of a decorative aquarium unless the gravel showing above the bottom frame of the container is camouflaged in some way.

An interesting variation on the conventional sub-gravel filter is shown in Figure 31. A reverse-flow action causes all debris to be trapped underneath the filter plate, thereby providing a cleaner gravel surface.

Both mechanical and biological filters can, of course, be operated by a water pump and this will enable larger flow-rates to be used if needed. The pump is usually situated below the level of

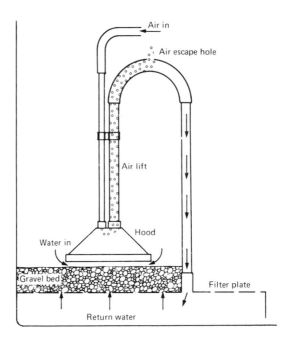

Fig 31 Illustration of the reverse-flow system which is used in some sub-gravel filters. The large area of the hood prevents gravel from being sucked up. In this arrangement, all debris is trapped *under* the filter plate *(After Vortex)*

the aquarium water so that it can be primed by siphoning initially and then if switched on and off at any time the system should be self-primed due to the automatic levelling action present. Of course, it must not leak or be opened while it is below the level of the aquarium, and its return or output pipe must always be above the water level to prevent the aquarium from being emptied through the pump. Water pumps nowadays can be made non-toxic, may not require lubrication and can have their electrical components completely isolated from the water. Some pumps are designed to run while submerged, for use inside the aquarium underwater.

5
Lighting and Electrical Installation

The basic principles which govern the role of light as a key factor in the aquatic environment have been discussed in Chapter 1. This chapter considers the equipment required to produce artificial light and the techniques which enable it to be used efficiently. Only electrical sources produce light of sufficient intensity for aquatic use. Domestic appliances, such as tungsten filament lamps or fluorescent tubes, are usually used, sometimes with minor modifications to suit them for use in aquaria.

Tungsten lamps (Figure 32a) have several serious disadvantages. Because they are relatively cheap to buy and easy to install they are often used with little thought, resulting in a short life for the lamps, inefficient use of their light and potentially dangerous situations. Bulbs made for domestic use are often designed so that the filament is only properly supported internally when the bulb is hanging vertically, and they are not meant to be moved or knocked while switched on. Thus their installation horizontally in shallow hoods (unfortunately the only kind commercially available), which must be moved to gain access for feeding and cleaning, can result in a considerable rate of replacement. Also, the usual type of domestic lamp-holder, which is often fitted in a metal hood, has poorly designed terminals which may collect condensation from the water surface below, thereby becoming dangerous. In addition, the lamps produce a lot of heat and this may overheat the surface water and cause distortion of any nearby plastic materials, often the hood itself. Their advantages are that they produce a type of light similar in many respects to sunlight, so that plants will flourish, they are relatively small and are available in a convenient range of values of light output and supply voltage.

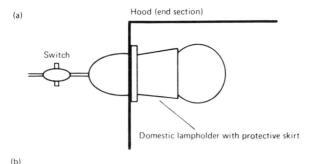

(a)

Hood (end section)

Switch

Domestic lampholder with protective skirt

(b)

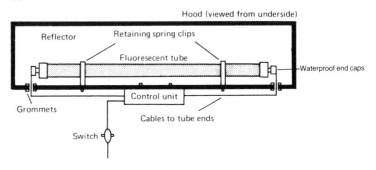

Hood (viewed from underside)

Reflector

Retaining spring clips

Fluorescent tube

Waterproof end caps

Grommets

Control unit

Cables to tube ends

Switch

Fig 32 Typical light fittings for the aquarium: (a) tungsten filament lamp; (b) fluorescent tube

For best results, bulbs should be mounted vertically and provided with air circulation to remove excess heat, and the aquarium should have a cover glass to keep condensation away from the light fittings. Industrial bulbs designed for horizontal use, known as 'rough service' lamps, can be used and have stronger filament supports. Reflectors or hoods for use with bulbs should be made so that the fish can be fed without disturbing the hood. When the aquarium is being cleaned, the lamps should be switched off and allowed sufficient time to cool before the hood is removed.

In most rectangular aquaria more than one lamp is needed to give an even spread of light over the whole area, but it is usually better to use, say, two powerful lamps rather than four weaker ones, as the absorption of light by the water is quite noticeable and low-powered lamps will adequately illuminate only the upper levels of the aquarium. Table 7 gives some idea of the light output of tungsten lamps. It should be remembered that

TABLE 7   LIGHT OUTPUT OF TUNGSTEN FILAMENT LAMPS

(All lamps have a rated life of 1000 hours)

Single coil — light output (lumens)

Watts	110V	240V
25	200	200
40	400	325
60	695	575
100	1,280	1,160
150	2,090	1,960
200	2,090	2,720
300	4,700	4,300
500	8,500	7,700
750	13,800	12,400
1,000	19,000	17,300
1,500	—	27,500

Coiled coil — light output at 240V

Watts	Lumens
40	390
60	665
100	1,260
150	2,075

TABLE 8   LIGHT OUTPUT OF FLUORESCENT TUBES

Type	Length (in)									
	standard						miniature			
Length (in)	60	48	42	36	24	18	21	12	9	6
Wattage	65	40	40	30	20	15	13	8	6	4
White	4700	2800	2800	2150	1100	800	750	420	250	100
Warm white	4600	2700	2700	2150	1100	800	750	420	250	—
Cool white	4450	2650	—	2050	1050	750	700	360	240	—
Natural	3400	2100	—	1600	800	600	—	—	—	—
Northlight/ col match	2700	1700	—	1250	700	500	—	—	—	—
Artificial daylight	2100	1200	—	—	500	—	—	—	—	—
Grolux	1300	810	—	530	340	200	—	—	—	—

In lumens after 2000 hours operation. New tubes will be 10–20% brighter.
60in, 48in and 24in tubes are 1½in diameter.
42in, 36in and 18in tubes are 1in diameter.
21in, 12in, 9in and 6in tubes are ⅝in diameter.

(*Courtesy* THORN EMI Lighting)

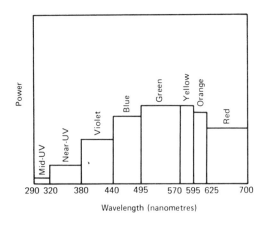

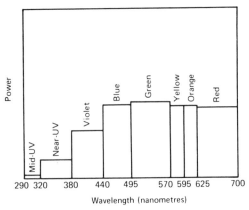

Fig 33 The remarkable similarity of the distribution of colours in natural light (below) and the fluorescent tube Tru-lite (*Courtesy Duro-Test International/ Emblem Engineering*)

where aquaria are mounted one above another any tungsten lamps in the lower installations will tend to heat the upper containers by convection, unless some insulation is fitted.

Nowadays aquarists use fluorescent lighting because of its several advantages. Originally the types of tubes available did not give off a natural kind of light and were so deficient in certain areas of the light spectrum that plants would not flourish. Better tubes are now available in the domestic range (Table 8) and, in addition, special types have been developed (eg Grolux, Tru-lite: see Figure 33) which simulate natural light and encourage plant growth. Grolux tubes are recommended even where plants are not grown, as they also emphasise the colours of the fish and other creatures, particularly the reds and pinks. The wavelength distributions of a number of typical tubes are shown in Figure 34.

Fluorescent lighting is not cheap to install but it is more efficient in use and the replacement rate is usually very low. It produces unwanted heat at a much lower rate than tungsten lamps and generates more light per watt of power consumed by the tube. The tube gives a good dispersion of light, but the power is governed by the length of the tube and it is not possible, for instance, to have a 50W tube only 30cm (1ft) long or

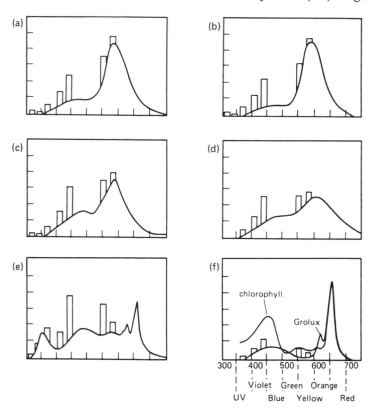

Fig 34 The distribution of colours in the light from a range of typical fluorescent tubes: (a) white; (b) warm white; (c) daylight; (d) natural; (e) artificial daylight; (f) Grolux with superimposition of the chlorophyl synthesis curve in plants (*Courtesy Thorn Lighting*)

a 10W tube 120cm (4ft) long, and this must be taken into account in the design of the system.

Associated with the fluorescent tube are a choke and a starter which are essential to its performance, shown on page 96 (Figure 32b). These may be supplied in a common case with the tube holders or mounted separately. Two fluorescent lighting circuits are shown in Figure 35. The auto-transformer system tends to eliminate flashing when the tube is first switched on and may also allow a long tube life. The choke is heavy and allowance should be made for this when building or buying a reflector, and the starter needs to be accessible for easy substitution if a fault arises. Some fittings may also have a capacitor in the circuit, as shown, but this is not usual in the low-powered lamps used in aquaria.

Once the aquarist is certain there are no loose connections, all fault finding in fluorescent systems is most easily done by sub-

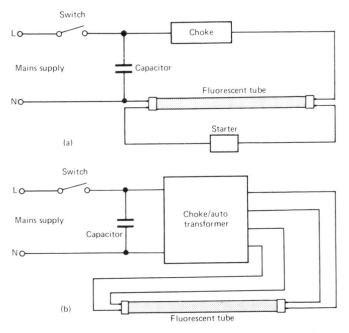

Fig 35 Circuits for fluorescent lighting systems using (a) an automatic starter, and (b) an auto transformer

stitution with new parts. The advice of a competent electrician is advisable in complicated installations.

Switches for fluorescent lighting should be of a higher current rating than those used for tungsten lamps of the same power, as the choke produces a power surge at the instant of switching on. For this reason multiple lighting systems should not be run from a common low-current switch but should be treated individually. It is recommended that each lamp installation should have a switch capable of carrying at least 5A current. Also, because of the influence of the choke, electric shocks received from this type of equipment are likely to be more severe than from some other sources and so every care should be taken to see that condensation, splashing or salt deposits from marine aquaria do not find their way on to or into the equipment. In this respect there is a ready market waiting for a properly-designed aquarium hood, as a good one does not seem to be available.

Combinations of tungsten and fluorescent lighting are often used to good effect. It seems that there may still be some radiation missing from individual fluorescent lamps which plants can obtain in a combined system, and also the problem of applying higher powers of light to small areas is made easier. If the installation conditions required for both types of lamp are met there are no technical difficulties in this kind of system.

Two useful lighting accessories are the dimmer and the time switch. The dimmer enables the aquarist to vary the lighting smoothly to any value up to full brilliance, so that by experiment an optimum system can be arrived at without expensive substitution. A time switch allows the period of illumination to be set automatically to suit the environment and also ensures day-to-day constancy. It is quite a simple thing to install and use; the type supplied for domestic appliances is most suitable and widely available. Both these accessories can be used together if connected one after the other in the supply line and both must of course be able to carry the full current drawn by the lighting circuit at any time.

Safety

In this chapter it is hoped to explain enough about aquarium electrical installations to enable the aquarist to install equipment in a safe and reliable manner. Many sources of information evade this question by quite correctly advising the aquarist to consult a competent electrician, as has already been mentioned. It is however a fact that when a person buys, say, a heater and a thermostat he does not often call in an electrician to wire up the circuit, but for various reasons does it himself. Having wired up a heater system which seems satisfactory, confidence is gained for more complex enterprises often with disastrous results. It is therefore felt that it is better to explain some electrical theory in simple terms and to discuss some simple methods, rather than to dismiss the subject with advice which, although good, will probably not be heeded. As an introduction, Figure 36 shows the electrical connections for a typical aquarium.

The normal mains electricity supply in the British Isles is 240V ac at 50 hertz. The letters 'ac' stand for 'alternating current' and show that the supply fluctuates in a cyclic fashion. A battery, for instance, supplies direct current (dc) which is continuous, and has a positive and negative terminal. An ac supply alternates between positive and negative at its terminals, ie one terminal is positive at one instant, negative at the next, then positive again, and so on, and the other terminal is always in the opposite condition. The speed at which this reversing process occurs is called the frequency of the supply and is measured in cycles per second, nowadays called hertz (Hz).

The voltage of the supply, 240V in Britain, is the 'pressure' of the electricity which is available and waiting to push the electric current into any load placed on the supply system. Thus the designation shows that the electricity available at the supply point is at 240V 'pressure' and cycling between positive and negative at a rate of 50 times per second.

The amount of electricity taken by a connected appliance is called the current and is measured in amperes, usually abbreviated to amps, and is determined by the power of that

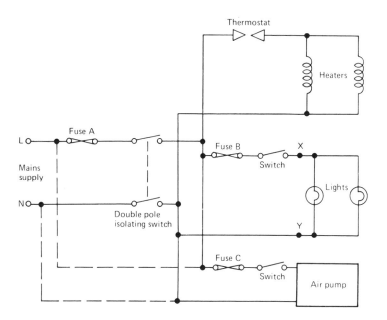

Fig 36 Electrical connections for a typical aquarium. Fuse A must be able to carry the whole current but B and C should be rated to match the lighting system and the air pump respectively. By this means, a fault which blows either fuse B or C does not affect the heating circuit. If there is a short circuit in the heating system, fuse A will blow and both the pump and the lights will fail. A fluorescent lamp can be substituted for the tungsten lamps by connecting at points X and Y. All switches and fuses must be rated to carry the required load. The dotted lines show an alternative arrangement in which a failure of the heating system does not affect the air pump, as will be necessary in a crowded aquarium

appliance, which is measured in watts. Because the amount of current taken by a particular appliance or load will depend also on the pressure of voltage available to push it into the appliance there is a simple relationship between these three properties which is expressed as:

Power = current x voltage
or
Watts = amps x volts

(There are further complications to the above equation in more complex circuits than are used for aquarium apparatus and where extremely high current values are drawn, but these do not concern us here and can be ignored.) Thus, if a heater is specified by the manufacturer as suitable for operation on a 240V supply and has a power of 100W the current it will draw can be calculated as follows:

Watts = amps x volts
Thus: amps = watts ÷ volts
           = 100 ÷ 240 = 0.417A

By approximating to a convenient round number it can be said that a 100W heater takes a current of just under half an amp. It may not seem important at first glance to know this fact, but the point is that electrical wiring, switches and other items through which the current flows on its way to any appliance are all designed to carry only a certain maximum current, and if this is exceeded either a fuse will blow to protect the circuit, or the wire or switch will overheat and be damaged, or a fire may start. It follows that when electrical apparatus is installed it is important to know the maximum value of current needed and then to use materials which can carry all of this current safely.

It can also be seen from the above that an appliance performs at its specified power only when it is connected to a supply system which provides the proper voltage. Thus a 240V light bulb applied to a 12V supply would only glow feebly, if at all, and a 12V lamp applied to a 240V supply would burn out immediately and might even explode. Some items such as heaters and light bulbs can work equally well on ac or dc supplies, provided the voltage is correct, but others such as air pumps and fluorescent lamps will work only with an ac supply. This last point is mentioned only as a matter of interest as there is no point in the aquarist considering the use of any other supply than the domestic one. Certain items can be bought, for instance some pumps for goldfish ponds, which operate at a lower voltage, but these are then supplied with a transformer which converts the normal mains voltage to that used by the appliance, and the whole apparatus is still plugged into the domestic supply system.

Installations of one or two average-sized aquaria in the home will not cause problems in electricity supply because their total current consumption will be low. For instance, two 3ft aquaria, each with two 75W heaters and two 40W lamps, have a power consumption of 460W. Adding a little for an air pump gives a total of 480W and then by repeating the calculation used previously we can derive a current consumption of 2A. As modern domestic installations are wired for 13A, or 5 or 15A in older systems, this set-up can be plugged into any convenient wall socket. Connecting cable and switches should have a current rating of 5A to allow for some safety margin.

Larger installations using electrical heating systems can be treated in the same way but eventually a point may be reached where the total current demand of the installation is greater than that which can be supplied by a domestic wall socket. This is where the competent electrician really must become involved because it will now be necessary to run a heavy duty cable from the main fuse box to wherever the aquaria are situated and to set up the necessary terminations and switches. In order to allow domestic wall socket circuits to be run below their maximum, so as to cater for other appliances in the house, a good general rule is that an independent system should be fitted up as soon as the total current consumption for the aquarium facility is more than 5A (assuming a 13A wall socket system).

Connections and cables in multiple immersion-heated systems are often a terrible mess when installed by the aquarist and are frequently downright dangerous. Badly-kept fish houses in particular often have damp atmospheres with condensation running down the walls, and this must be eliminated and all wiring kept short and tidy to ensure safe working and reliability. Lighting circuits should be fused and switched independently of heating circuits so that a fault in one system does not affect the other. Any small air pumps can be supplied from the lighting circuit or from their own separate line. Amateur electricians frequently use insulation tape to separate twisted wire junctions from each other and this is not recommended as a reliable or safe method since damp can often get in and the tape deteriorates in time. All connections should be made in enclosed boxes or by means of interlinked wall sockets (Figure 37), this last method having the advantage that components can be replaced without interfering with the rest of the installation.

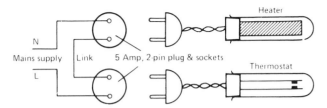

Fig 37 Connections for a single heater system using interlinked wall sockets

The question of earthing has caused a lot of controversy amongst aquarists because it is very difficult to apply a suitable method to aquaria. The principle behind the idea of earthing electrical appliances is that if a fault develops which, for instance, results in the metal casing of an electric iron becoming live, then if that casing is effectively connected to the earth of the supply system a large current will flow from the live terminal to the earth with the result that the fuses blow out immediately to make everything safe. Various difficulties are encountered in aquaria, and the problem is not really capable of solution; it is instructive to consider why this is so.

The usual aquarium construction, whereby the water is contained within glass, putty, plastics, glass-fibre and other materials which are all electrical insulators, means that should the water become live, for instance through a cracked heater tube, there is no conducting material in direct contact with the water to which an earth wire can be attached. The only usable, efficient conducting materials are metals, usually copper, but even if an aquarium frame were made of copper it would still be insulated wholly or partially, from the water, by the glass and sealant. Thus the only effective earth would be a terminal actually in the water, but this is not possible because of the toxic effects of submerged metals on small living creatures. It is well known, for instance, that particles from new copper water piping in extremely low concentrations will kill fish easily.

Fortunately water is not one of the best conductors of electricity and if the aquarist puts a hand into a live tank, and is suitably insulated by shoes, clothes and carpeting which are dry, he will not usually receive a shock which has the full capability of the supply behind it, although it will still be unpleasant (Figure 38). However, if he has one hand immersed in a live aquarium and then touches an earth terminal, such as a metal tank frame connected to the supply earth but insulated from the live water by the glass and putty, then the full current available may flow through his body on its way to that earth (Figure 38), with probably fatal results.

Fig 38 Earthing dangers: (a) without an earthing point, the aquarist will draw current from live water via his shoes, floor coverings etc, which will provide some limited protection; (b) when the frame of the container is earthed, the aquarist runs the risk of having a large current flow through his body from live water if he touches the frame

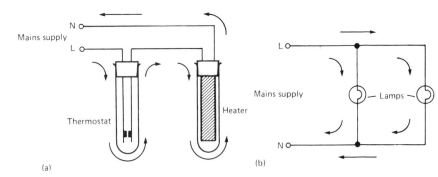

Fig 39 (a) Series and (b) parallel electrical connections commonly met with in the aquarium. The arrows represent current flows

It would therefore seem that the aquarist must risk any shocks which may come along and must minimise their possible effect by reliable installation and wiring and dry conditions. It is better to do without ineffective earths, which if touched at the wrong time as explained above would in fact make things far worse. Now that some metal-framed aquaria and their stands are being coated in plastic and nylon the temptation to earth these is less and this is probably a very good thing. All-glass aquaria do not have frames at all of course. If sufficient water gains entry into an item of immersible equipment it may short out the live and neutral terminals directly and thus cause the fuses to blow, rendering everything safe. Unfortunately it is often possible to get a shock from an aquarium long before this happens, and indeed it may never happen at all if for some reason only the live side of the appliance is in contact with the water.

Finally, two electrical terms with which the aquarist may meet are 'series' and 'parallel' which are used to describe connection configurations. For instance, if a thermostat and heater are connected together as in Figure 39a they are said to be in series with each other because the current has to flow through the thermostat to get to the heater. In a parallel connection, such as where two lamps use the same supply (Figure 39b), the current flows through each one independently of the other, and one can be removed without affecting the other.

6
Foods and Feeding

Most non-aquatic animals can be fed quite easily but in fish-keeping feeding is an acquired skill calling for understanding and discipline on the part of the aquarist because the success of the whole environment will depend on the proper introduction of food. Feeding is therefore as much a technique as a routine and food is a true factor in the environment (see Chapter 1).

While food has the obvious property of keeping alive the inhabitants of the aquarium, it also has many other influences. Growth, health and general well-being are determined by proper feeding. The ability of species to live together, their reproductive potential, their condition and decorative appearance, and many other characteristics, are all dependent on the feeding methods used. These same characteristics are, of course, also dependent on other environmental factors but the point is that, even if these other factors are perfect, bad feeding will spoil everything.

Aquatic creatures are very adaptable and will quite easily become accustomed to a variety of foods which are not found in their natural habitats. This fact is of immense benefit to the aquarist, who is thus able to use foods which are easily obtainable. It does not mean, however, that a new 'unnatural' food can be used thoughtlessly because it may be that while it suits the creatures which eat it, it may have some property which has an extremely detrimental effect on the management of the environment as a whole.

Frequency of feeding is important. Most of the commonly kept fish are of the smaller shoaling kinds and in nature these will feed often or continually if conditions (especially temperature) are favourable. In an artificial environment where constant favourable conditions are maintained the fish may take food frequently and therefore need to be fed quite often, particularly when they are young. In order to avoid the consequences of overfeeding, aquarists are usually advised as a safety measure to feed infrequently, and because most people work away from home it is easy to settle into a routine of providing food only twice daily at the most. This practice goes against the needs of many fish and inhibits their development. Fortunately, fish do absorb nutrients from the water through their body surfaces which allow them to exist for long periods without eating; but this does not mean that they will thrive when food is not available, and thus their development can be retarded. Some fish and other creatures which are predatory feed only infrequently but in most aquaria these are the exception rather than the rule. All young fish and many adults should, if possible, be offered food of the right kind as often as they will take it. If the aquarist is unable to supply food at frequent intervals then methods of feeding must be worked out which allow suitable foods to be available in the aquarium for long periods but which do not lead to any deterioration in environmental conditions as a result.

Overfeeding is a common fault amongst inexperienced and disinterested aquarists. The term 'overfeeding' applies to the environment, not to its inhabitants, and if it is viewed in this way it is easier to understand its implications. A fish can hardly be overfed because it will simply refrain from eating when full, but the artificial environment can easily be overloaded with food in such amounts that its cleansing facilities cannot cope with the resulting deterioration and pollution.

When fish are fed heavily, say with a commercial dry food, they eat as much as possible until their initial hunger is sated. They then cruise about picking up odd bits, playing with them, swallowing some and rejecting others, and finally perhaps not feeding at all until after a period of digestion. In the meantime the uneaten food settles in the gravel and other niches, absorbs water and begins to rot. When the fish are willing to feed again most of these uneaten remains are unavailable to them, and unpalatable anyway, and so are left untouched. If the aquarist now administers another heavy feed the process is repeated so that a continuous build-up of uneaten food is generated, which completes a vicious circle because the resulting pollution eventually affects the inhabitants and causes them to go off their food due to ill-health — and so the situation becomes even worse.

In effect, overfeeding prevents successful completion of the nitrogen cycle and an accumulation of toxic minerals occurs. The aquarist may reduce the effects of this by water changing or by constant, heavy filtration, but this does not solve the basic problem and only makes more work. Many potentially good aquarists are lost from the hobby because they simply do not understand this problem and do not realise that the cause of much of the trouble they experience maintaining their aquaria may quite simply be a result of incorrect feeding.

The solution to the problem, then, is either to feed the fish often but with only as much food as will be completely consumed in a short while, or to use foods which stay alive until eaten or at least do not deteriorate quickly and do not become inaccessible. The fish should be kept just slightly hungry so that they will search for food between feeds and will take the trouble to dig out odd pieces from crevices, thus generally helping to keep the environment clean. The environment's capacity for completing the nitrogen cycle is usually fully taken up in dealing with the fish's wastes and ideally should never be called on to deal with uneaten food. Of course some food will always escape the fish, no matter how careful the aquarist may be, but this amount must be so small that its effects are negligible. Certainly many people put so much food into aquaria that more is left uneaten than is consumed, and this situation causes the greater proportion of all troubles encountered by the novice.

Children and visitors must never be allowed to feed the fish for amusement as they invariably are heavy-handed in the cause of well-meant generosity. Aquaria in schools, hospitals and other such places inevitably suffer from uneducated feeding and then create the impression among the general public that fishkeeping is dirty and smelly and requires constant work — which, of course, is true if feeding practices are incorrect.

Variety in the fish's diet is not always as important as some people, particularly advertisers, would have us believe. As long as the diet of the fish meets all their requirements, and the aquarist's convenience as well, there is no need to go to too much trouble to provide other items 'for a change'. Variety in feeding is necessary only when it provides essential dietary requirements which may not all be present in one particular food. The merits of the various foods available should be studied and a composite diet provided to meet the fish's specific requirements. There is no point in alternating a good food with one which is different but of far less benefit.

The main substances required to form a balanced diet for aquarium fish, and indeed all vertebrates, are proteins, carbohydrates, fats and oils, minerals and vitamins, and an understanding of their functions will prove useful. Proteins are the foundation of the diet and its most essential component for they encourage growth and the replacement of body tissues. Proteins are, chemically, compounds of carbon, nitrogen, oxygen, hydrogen and various trace elements. They can be classified either as animal or vegetable depending on their origin and for aquarium use can be obtained from live creatures and plants. Carbohydrates act as a fuel in that they provide energy and body heat, and are obtainable from starchy foods such as biscuit meal and oatmeal. Fats and oils similarly promote energy and warmth and nourish the nervous system. The body can store these substances against times of shortage. They are best obtained as constituents of foods such as meat and fish. Minerals such as iron, calcium and phosphorus help to build the bones, teeth, muscles and circulatory system and are common in many foods as trace ingredients. Vitamins are active organic compounds which provide protection against disease and generally facilitate the body functions. Vegetable foods, or creatures which feed directly on them, are the primary sources of vitamins in aquaria. Vitamin A, for example, is formed in the body from a compound called carotene which is found in plants and this is used by the fish to develop and intensify colouring. Vitamin B is similarly obtained from plants and one of its properties is to assist in the correct functioning of the digestive organs. The importance of vegetable foods as suppliers of vitamins is paramount and many aquarists fail in this respect by not providing enough green food.

It is convenient to classify the various foods commonly used into four categories, namely: natural foods, cultured foods, table foods and prepared dry foods. These are dealt with below under their individual headings.

Natural Foods

Natural foods are those which fish feed on in the wild state. Some little trouble is involved in their collection but they do seem to provide something which other foods lack, and are especially good for rearing young fish and for bringing adults into breeding condition. Some live foods can be bought but their condition cannot always be relied on as some types do not store well.

Earthworms are one of the best foods for all fish, either whole for larger specimens or broken or mashed up for small fish. A certain amount of dirt and slime comes with them and should be washed off before use. They must not be taken from ground which has been treated with weedkillers or fertilisers. They can be bred and encouraged to collect in compost heaps or holes filled with tea leaves and kitchen scraps. They flourish best in dark, damp conditions and moderate temperatures. Earthworms are ideal for bringing the larger fish into breeding condition, but it may be found that the quantities eaten by very large fish makes their acquisition a demanding job. They live for some time in water if left uneaten but will often burrow into the gravel before death occurs, so that removal of the bodies is usually impossible. Feeding should therefore be carried out carefully and sparingly. Small worms called brandlings, found in manure and some compost heaps, are not good for aquarium use as they exude a thick yellow fluid when damaged which will cause problems in a closed habitat.

Various small creatures under the general name of Daphnia are used by aquarists. As collected or purchased a quantity of Daphnia often contains a multitude of organisms, such as cyclops and rotifers, all of which are good fish foods. Daphnia are crustaceans and have a hard exterior skeleton which provides needed roughage in the fish's diet. They are found in shallow water in farm ponds, ditches, canals, in fact in almost any still water containing even smaller organisms, such as Infusoria, on which they feed. Cattle droppings or green water thus indirectly stimulate the development of Daphnia and their population level is apparently also dependent on weather conditions. There are several varieties of Daphnia, of different size and colour, and some of these seem to be seasonal.

Daphnia can be collected simply by netting with a fine mesh. They will not tolerate crowded conditions for long and do not transfer well to unmatured tap-water. They must be kept cool and if stored for any time should be maintained in well-aerated conditions. Some larger creatures, such as beetles and various insect larvae, are often caught with Daphnia and these can be useful in the aquarium if they are eaten by larger fish. Generally, however, larger pond creatures should be removed as they may attack small fish. The pond water acquired with the Daphnia can be put into the aquarium with them if it is clean and may be beneficial in providing many other microscopic organisms which the fish will also eat. Daphnia must of course never be collected from any body of water containing any kind of fish life. All wild fish have parasites and these will usually fluorish in an aquarium, and, being small, are extremely difficult to eradicate. Daphnia can be introduced into freshwater environments in quite reasonable quantities as they live for some time and are useful where infrequent feeding is practised. In salt water they die quickly and so must be used more carefully. Daphnia can be bred at home in shallow ponds fed with cow dung or kitchen scraps to produce thick Infusoria colonies, but the amount may not make the effort and inconvenience worth while. Young fish particularly benefit from large quantities of small Daphnia in their diet.

Tubifex worms are obtained commercially from mud in tidal estuaries, such as the Thames in London, and from sewer outlets and similar places. Collection is unpleasant and specialised, requiring a knowledge of local conditions and equipment such as sieves and waders. They can, however, be bought at most aquarists' suppliers at reasonable prices for small quantities and it would not benefit the average aquarist to collect his own. They cannot be completely recommended because of various disadvantages. Due to the conditions existing in their natural habitat they require thorough washing and cleaning with a suitable commercial preparation before use, and will easily die unless kept in cold running water. As bought they may or may not be clean and fresh, depending on the previous treatment received, and those which are unhealthy must not be fed to the fish. It is difficult to be sure what state they are in. Some varieties of tubifex are said to be parasitic and able to live inside, and later eat their way out of, fish which swallow them whole. Any which settle in a gravel bed will quickly establish themselves so well that only certain fish can then make use of them. They live in the gravel for some time but die eventually, especially at tropical temperatures, and their resulting decomposition can cause pollution if they are present in large numbers. Boils, gill disorders and unexplained deaths are a feature of fish fed on this food, so the aquarist is advised against its use.

Glassworms, properly called gnat larvae, occur mainly in cold weather in waters containing decaying vegetable matter. They are small free-swimming creatures about half an inch long and have a transparent body which is usually horizontal in the water. They are collected in the same way as Daphnia and are often found with them. They have the advantage that they can be crowded together for transport and storage, and make an excellent food for medium-sized and adult fish. They are able to catch fish fry with a hooked appendage at their heads and so must not be put in with small fish. Their food value seems excellent and they live in the aquarium for long periods if uneaten.

Aquarium snails can be considered a natural food. When they achieve an excess population, instead of being thrown away, or killed with proprietary liquids, they can be crushed and fed to the fish. Very large fish, such as Oscars, will crack the shells themselves, but they are too tough for most other fish. Snails are a good food that should be used at every opportunity and certainly not wasted.

Cultured Foods

Over many years, knowledgeable aquarists have developed methods of culturing and breeding satisfactorily several small food animals which are extremely useful, especially when rearing young fish. Most of them are available commercially in the form of 'starter' cultures, or even eggs, and they can fairly easily be propagated in quantity. Table 9 gives a summary of various cultured foods.

The smallest of these food animals are Infusoria, the collective name given to colonies of microscopic organisms occurring naturally in sunlit waters containing organic refuse. They can be collected from ponds and water butts but if regularly required in reasonable quantities they should be cultured artificially. Infusoria are practically the only live food small enough, and capable of being produced in sufficient quantities, for the newly-hatched fry of many of the smaller fish. It is imperative that aquarists wishing to breed any of the smaller egglaying fish

TABLE 9   CULTURED FOODS — SUMMARY OF METHODS

Type	Culture medium	Temp range	Food	Development time	Culture lifetime
Infusoria	Decaying vegetable matter in water	65–70°F	Bacteria in culture	10–20 days	Used all at once
Microworm	Wet cooked oatmeal	70–80°F	Oatmeal	3–5 days	Approx 14 days
Brine Shrimp	Salt solution	75–80°F	None	Hatch in 24 hours at 80°F	Use as soon as possible
Grindal worm	2:1 peat/ sand mixture kept damp	65–75°F	Oatmeal paste	14 days	Indefinite if properly cared for
Whiteworm		55–70°F	Wet bread		

develop a satisfactory method of culturing Infusoria in quantity. There are several old-fashioned methods commonly recommended but those which involve standing containers of culture medium outdoors in the sun are not sufficiently reliable for consistent production, as fluctuations of temperature and light cannot be controlled.

The Infusoria culture is produced by placing crushed lettuce, banana skins or other vegetable matter in a container and then pouring boiling water over it to initiate its breakdown and subsequent rotting. After a little time, say twenty-four hours, the bulk of the culture can be made up with cold water to fill the container, but this must not contain live organisms which might eat the Infusoria. The Infusoria find their way into the culture by means of air-borne spores and the initial population should be acquired automatically. It is vital to keep the culture at a minimum temperature of 65°F (18.5°C). After a few days the culture becomes turbid and at this time may not be very pleasant. Many aquarists mistake this for the completed culture but at this stage it has no value as a fish food. It is, in fact, a bacterial culture and the Infusoria multiply by consuming the bacteria, so that after about a week and a half the turbidity clears and the culture becomes transparent and practically odourless. Gentle aeration is useful to maintain aerobic conditions, otherwise it may need frequent stirring by hand. After three weeks the culture should be really thick and the Infusoria can be seen collectively as a shimmering mass when the container is viewed against the light. If it is desired to use one culture per day a rotation system of about twenty containers (eg large sweet jars) must be set up such that as one is used another is started. This of course requires space and some artificial heating may be needed to maintain the minimum temperature, as well as illumination. If a continuous supply is not needed the culture should be started three weeks before it will be required. To feed the fish, the liquid culture is simply poured into the aquarium. It should be noted that Infusoria consume oxygen, so any overfeeding may cause problems in crowded environments.

For the young of the common livebearers and the larger

egglayers the ideal first food is the Brine Shrimp (*Artemia salina*). This is a small salt-water organism whose eggs are collected commercially and, as they are storable, can be hatched out as required. There is some controversy as to whether they should be used for freshwater fish for long periods because of the salt content in their bodies, but certainly for the initial period, until the fry can take larger foods, they are excellent. A salt environment is necessary for hatching the eggs but this need not be as perfect as that used for keeping marine fish. The artificial salt-water mixes sold for marine fishkeeping do give a better hatching of the eggs, but as the water used is generally spoilt after a few hatches this might be considered expensive. A good general method is to use a plastic bucket containing a solution of ordinary block salt, or 'aquarium salt' as sold in shops, made up to a density of 1.025. The temperature of the solution will determine the hatching time and usually at 80°F (27°C) the shrimps appear after about twenty-four hours. A heater and thermostat can be included to maintain this temperature. The young shrimps also benefit from turbulence and aerobic conditions, so aeration can be applied to advantage. A more sophisticated method is illustrated in Figure 40. A triangular or funnel-shaped container with an airstone fitted at the inverted apex ensures that the eggs cannot settle anywhere and are thus always properly exposed to the brine solution. The best results are obtained if the unit is big enough to hold its own heating system for constant temperature control. Tubes for drainage and shrimp collecting can be fitted if required.

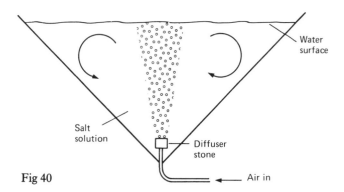

Fig 40

The culture technique described above makes use of a warm salt-water environment of a very simple kind which is easy to set up but will only hatch a certain number of eggs before becoming spoilt. Therefore for continuous production a rotation system is again needed, but because the hatching time is quite fast not so many containers will be required as for Infusoria, three usually being sufficient. The individual baby shrimps are just discernable to the eye and in quantity are seen as a bright orange cloud in the water. When they are about to be removed for feeding, aeration should be stopped and time allowed for the water to settle, when it will be seen that the empty eggshells will either float or sink and the live shrimps will swim in mid-water, from where they can easily be siphoned off into a fine net. They are light-sensitive and collect together if a small bulb is placed near a convenient point. Some aquarists like to wash the shrimps to remove any salt before they are fed to the fish, but this is a minor point, especially where the fry receive shrimps for perhaps only two weeks. The shrimps do not live long in freshwater aquaria, so must be used carefully, but they will live and grow in marine environments if uneaten. Many marine aquarists simply put the eggs into their aquaria and allow them to hatch there. This method is extremely convenient but after a time the accretion of empty shells may detract from the decorative appearance of the aquarium.

Brine Shrimp can be reared easily to the adult stage if they are kept in a more stable environment and fed on Infusoria (and one another). They are interesting aquatically as well as being good food for larger fish, but the process is as troublesome as rearing the fish themselves, so is not often practised. Marine fish-keepers can do it in any old water which is not polluted.

Microworms are another small food easily accepted by small fish. They are cultured in trays containing a thick paste of cooked oatmeal, kept at a temperature of about 75°F (24°C). A small quantity of microworms are needed initially to start the culture and these then multiply rapidly to the point where many of them leave the medium and move on to the sides of the tray. They can then be collected from there with a fine brush and fed directly to the fish. A culture usually lasts about a fortnight before becoming foul, when it can be replaced with a new one seeded from the original. The system is quite simple and, provided the temperature is maintained and the culture is not allowed to dry out, there should be no problems. As with the previous cultures, if a good continuous supply is required a rotation system of replacement can be used.

Grindal worms are larger and are bred in shallow boxes containing a mixture of two parts peat to one part fine sand (building sand is ideal). The culture is kept warm and damp and again a starter culture is used initially. The worms are fed on oatmeal paste which is placed on top of the peat under a cover glass. When the worms have developed in sufficient quantity many of them will move on to the underside of the glass and can readily be removed from there. The peat should be dug over periodically to prevent caking and eventually replaced with fresh material if the culture goes sour. The size of the grindal worm makes it a very acceptable second food for young fish and it can be a beneficial permanent part of the diet of any of the smaller fish at the adult stage. The whole point about Grindal and also Whiteworm cultures (see below) is that the aquarist must not take away the worms faster than they can be replaced otherwise the supply will obviously decline.

Whiteworms are larger than Grindal but otherwise similar, and often a culture may contain both types together. They are bred in peat cultures in the same way although larger containers are recommended, such as plastic seed-trays. The cultures should be kept in a warm but not hot place, which should be damp and dark. The most convenient food is simply a piece of wet bread and if other conditions are correct this will be all that is needed. Many aquarists use porridge, custard and all manner of things as food for their cultures, but there is no point in such complications if a simpler method will produce the same results. Every aquarist can benefit from a healthy supply of whiteworm whatever his aquatic interests, as it is relished by all adult fish, including marines, and is excellent for bringing adults into breeding condition. At least one culture should be kept for use when other live foods are not available. One point with peat cultures is that they tend to become populated with other creatures as well as the worms for which they are intended. These 'nits', 'fleas' and so on do not particularly affect the worms or harm aquarium inhabitants but they do make it advisable to keep the cultures out of the house in a shed or garage. If these other inhabitants become too troublesome the culture is best renewed with fresh peat, or carefully cleared with a vacuum cleaner.

Drosophila, a genus of small wingless fruit-fly developed by scientists for experimental use, is a very good food for fish and can be cultured in glass bottles containing a warm fermenting fruit mash. Initial supplies may be obtained from a biological or school supplier, and will contain complete culturing instructions, but the general use of Drosophila as food is not recommended due to the trouble and inconvenience involved and the poor yield resulting by comparison with, say, a good whiteworm culture. Some problem fish which eat only insects might benefit from the use of Drosophila but generally its culture is hardly worth while.

Table Foods

Almost anything which we eat ourselves can be fed with advantage to fish, providing it can be supplied in a suitable form and does not lead to pollution in the aquarium. It is obviously not possible to throw the leftovers into the fish tank instead of into the dog's dish but with care use can be made of a good selection of normal domestic foods.

First and foremost come cooked peas. Fish invariably do not get enough green food and peas are the simplest means of rectifying this. After cooking, the transparent shell should be removed and the whole pea dropped into the water in one lump to avoid clouding. All sorts of meat and fish products are very welcome provided they are not too tough or greasy and do not disperse easily in the water. Foods which remain in lumps are best as the fish will break them up as they need them and if the food remains uneaten the lump form retards deterioration. Large unwanted pieces can also be removed more easily. Examples include boiled liver, bacon, roe, fish, lettuce, spinach and occasionally cheese. New foods may not be taken eagerly on introduction so it is wise to feed very carefully until the fish become used to them. It may pay to introduce a little with a more familiar food at first. Commercial pet foods which are not too soft or greasy, such as cat biscuits and the drier dog meats, go a lot further for the same cost than commercial fish foods.

Large fish such as Oscars are often kept in relatively small containers. A 10in fish in a 3ft aquarium is rather like a goldfish in a glass bowl and must be fed extremely carefully if pollution is to be avoided. Most fish of this kind have teeth in their throats and when, for instance, they eat lumps of meat many fine particles are expelled through their gills and into the water, with obvious disadvantages. Experiments have shown that the way to overcome this difficulty is to use a food which the fish cannot chew easily and therefore swallow whole. Uncooked lean bacon performs this function nicely and keeps the environment clean even though the fish is receiving large quantities of food daily. The absence of mastication does not seem to have any ill effect as long as sensibly sized pieces are provided.

Dry Foods

Commercially packed dry fish foods are on the whole well-prepared and quite suitable for use if several points are understood. Their most damaging quality is the ease with which they can pollute the environment when used incorrectly. Due to the methods of preparation most are sensitive to water and quickly rot away if left uneaten in the aquarium. As mentioned repeatedly in this book, large quantities of uneaten food will ruin any environment and much care must therefore be taken. It is recommended that fish living mainly on dry foods be fed four or five times daily so that only a little food need be given at any one time. Even then, in inexperienced hands this will often be too much, particularly in partially-populated aquaria.

Dry foods are extremely expensive compared to other commodities. Even in the small quantities sold to aquarists the cost can be prohibitive if a large number of fish are kept. It is doubtful whether any commercial fisheries or public aquaria use fishfood as the aquarist buys it, even though it can be bought in bulk more cheaply. The aquarist's best approach is to regard all commercial dry foods as stop-gaps for emergency use and perhaps as a provider of roughage to assist the fish's digestive processes if other foods which perform this function, such as Daphnia, are not available. Certainly any good aquarist should never need to use dry foods as the basis of the fish's diet. Many prepared foods are sold as being especially for coldwater, or tropical, or marine, fish. While there may be some slight benefit to be gained by a particular type of fish from one particular formula, most formulae will be eaten by any fish which takes dry food. The thrifty aquarist can economise for instance by using goldfish foods for other fish, as these are usually cheaper, although it must be said that the commonly sold biscuit meal is not even recommended for goldfish.

Many fish of course will simply not take prepared food in any form at all and these must be fed in other ways even at some inconvenience to the aquarist. Some of them can be trained to take fresh meat but many will eat only live creatures. It must never be imagined that when a fish eats dry foods because nothing else is ever offered to it that this food is adequate for its needs. Many people who keep community aquaria provide only one brand of dry food and feed only this to every fish in their care, regardless of species or size or any other factor. This attitude is only to be deplored and shows either ignorance or a complete lack of consideration for the requirements of the fish.

7
Breeding and Quantity Production

Sooner or later most aquarists become involved in one way or another in breeding fish. The first baby livebearer born usually sets up a reaction which invariably stimulates interest and participation in the subject. Methods for breeding various species of fish have a number of factors in common, and this chapter will principally be concerned with these important generalities. It is not within the scope of this book to give details of the particular requirements of individual species, but the aquarist requiring specialised information on certain fish will find that the relevant publications are widely available. Each case should be treated systematically as a separate exercise until full knowledge and reliable methods are evolved for that species. Communication between serious aquarists is usually good and our system of societies and associations makes for the free exchange of much hard-won information. The beginner should never be afraid to ask, or reluctant to discuss personal experiences, because there is so much to learn that the pooling of data and ideas is essential.

Before discussing the techniques involved, the ethics of the situation must be considered. Fish must never be treated as mere playthings and if a species is to be encouraged to reproduce it must be provided with the best possible chances of success. Breeding does not end with the production of live fry but rather with a properly-reared group of young adults. It is quite easy to obtain numerous fry from very many species with only a minimum of trouble. The secret is to rear them to be true representatives of their species. The aquarist must realise that buying or breeding a fish means taking on an obligation to ensure that the creature has the best habitat that can be provided. There is no point in breeding fish to be eaten by others or to be permanently stunted by overcrowding and bad feeding. The common practice of culling healthy fry to provide space for a selected few is ethically wrong and unless the aquarist can hope to raise and care for the whole number of fry produced at a spawning the exercise should not be initiated.

In community environments, or where the aquarist has only one aquarium, it is very difficult to take note of ethical factors. Livebearers will reproduce frequently and egglayers may spawn quite often. These fry and eggs will be eaten by the other inhabitants almost immediately and there is little the aquarist can do about it, except to keep only fish of a single sex in any particular species. This is hardly ever practised and indeed a lot of interest and enjoyment would be lost if it were, because the whole idea of studying the fish's habits and way of life argues for the presence of both sexes. It would seem then that we must accept the losses involved in this situation as inevitable. The loss of the spawn of egglayers is not perhaps so important but to see young livebearers gobbled up can be distressing and could be avoided if only one sex of these were kept in mixed aquaria. To avoid the loss of fry in this way many aquarists attempt to retain them by the use of small containers, so-called 'breeding traps', or by dividing off a small portion of the aquarium. This practice is suitable only for a very small number of certain hardy species and must be recognised as such. It is no good putting, say, thirty baby guppies in a container which holds only two pints of water and then expecting them to grow and live normally. It is better not to breed them at all than to subject them to this treatment.

It can be argued of course that in nature young fry provide an item in the diet of many adult fish and other creatures and are in fact produced so prolifically because of this; but the aquarist must not fall into the trap of excusing callous actions with this argument because once safe, reasonable living conditions have been provided for the adults, it is hypocritical to ignore the obligations to the fry and to consider them expendable. Nature is cruel, but there are no similar requirements for the aquarist.

Let us assume that the serious aquarist wishes to breed a few fish to gain further knowledge and enjoyment of the hobby and is willing to provide the extra facilities needed and to carry out the work involved so that the resulting fish are a worthwhile acquisition. How should the exercise be approached?

Fish can be categorised into those which produce live young (livebearers) and those which produce spawn (egglayers). Furthermore, the overall breeding process can conveniently be divided into three stages, ie preparation, the breeding act, and rearing the fry. The subject of preparation and rearing are fairly similar for both livebearers and egglayers so can be treated in common; but for the breeding act itself a distinction can be made between the two types of fish and indeed the egglayers can be sub-divided even further as will be seen.

The question of the use of suitable breeding stock is a thorny one. Most aquarists who are breeding for the first time will tend to use whatever parents are at hand, without going to a lot of trouble to find the best available specimens; this may prove satisfactory or it may not. There are two basic types of fish bred by aquarists, those which are either wild or retain all the characteristics of the wild species although bred in captivity, and those which are a cultivated variety of a wild species and differ considerably from the natural fish. These two types require different methods of breeding and selection of breeding stock.

Those fish which have been bred in captivity for many generations and yet still closely resemble the wild type are in fact a pure strain developed and fixed by nature. On the other hand, cultivated fish such as the fancy goldfish, Guppies and Siamese Fighters have all resulted from attempts by man to alter nature's pure strains. Once obtained, the new strain is maintained through generations of selective breeding in an effort to accentuate any new characteristics still further and, having reached the desired level of accentuation, to fix it in the new strain. Such accentuations may be considered beautiful or otherwise, but as far as nature is concerned these 'altered' fish are undesirable freaks which can only weaken the naturally fixed pure strain. Therefore there is always the certainty present that if the cultivated fish are allowed to breed indiscriminately they will eventually revert back to the pattern of the natural strain. It is thus essential to practise careful selective breeding in order to keep the strain in its altered state.

With natural fish, however, indiscriminate breeding can be practised since there can be no reversion to a wild form. Indiscriminate breeding is in fact essential to maintain the strain at its best. While a natural strain may appear to be improved a little in captivity in such characteristics as size and intensity of colour, these are not necessarily alterations to the strain itself but may only be improvements to the individual fish caused by better living conditions and the removal of many of the hazards which occur in nature. It follows therefore that the selection of breeding stock for a natural strain is considerably easier than for a cultivated strain because we are not trying to alter nature's pattern. From time to time freak fish will be produced from a natural strain, for instance Tiger Barbs which have part of one of the black bars missing. These fish must not be used as breeding stock since the fault will probably be reproduced in their offspring, either immediately or in a later generation. From this then it can be seen that to keep a natural strain at its best, close inbreeding must be avoided at all costs.

To breed a natural species, the aquarist must start off by obtaining male and female breeding stocks which are not closely related. Enough fish should be obtained to make up as many breeding pairs as can be managed thus allowing the adults to pair up indiscriminately and ensuring that the fry in one batch are not closely related to other batches. If it is difficult to obtain unrelated breeding stock, as may be the case with some of the rarer species, the aquarist may be forced to start off with close inbreeding. Provided the initial pair are true representatives of the natural strain a little close inbreeding can be tolerated if circumstances make this unavoidable but, unless the strain is to deteriorate, fresh unrelated blood must be brought in as soon as possible. As well as amplifying freak characteristics, close inbreeding will introduce defects such as lack of vitality and delicate health if carried on indefinitely. This is why cultivated fish are often much harder to keep than their wild counterparts.

Indiscriminate breeding of a natural strain is made easier in many cases by the fact that many species spawn as a shoal. This is termed 'flock breeding'. The danios and most of the barbs are good examples of such species. Several pairs can be placed together and will freely interbreed. Wherever possible, flock breeding should be encouraged as this is nature's own way of avoiding close inbreeding.

The propagation of a cultivated fish strain is far more challenging to the serious breeder and demands a lot more effort and experience. As explained above, nature considers these fish to be abnormal and any mistakes by the breeder in the selection of breeding stock will result in the strains starting to revert to the wild form. If breeding stock is used which has partly reverted then the rate of reversion will be accelerated. Furthermore, while the breeder is trying to produce in a strain those altered characteristics which are considered desirable, other traits will probably be encountered which may be undesirable and even detrimental. Even more intensive selective breeding may then be necessary to eliminate these undesired alterations without in the process losing the original requirements.

Let us suppose that an aquarist has a good natural strain of fish and in one of the batches of young there appears a freak fish which is different in some characteristic. Let us further suppose that this new feature is so attractive that the aquarist decides to attempt to establish a cultivated strain of fish which will eventually breed true in this altered form. The first step will be to give the freak fish the best food available and to attend to its environmental conditions with the utmost care so as to bring it to maturity in as good a condition as possible. This fish is then backcrossed either to its father or mother, depending on its sex, or, if this is not possible for some reason, to its brother or sister. Unless the brother or sister exhibits the same freak characteristic, however, this method is not so reliable. All the young from the first backcrossing are then kept and reared to maturity in the best possible conditions. It may be found that the important characteristic does not appear in the first generation at all. This does not mean that it is lost but that it is only 'covered up' by more dominant characteristics which still exist in the strain. The way to uncover the freak characteristic is to mate the original fish with all the fish of the opposite sex in the first generation, when the characteristic should appear in a reasonable proportion in the second generation. If the second generation fish which show the alteration are now backcrossed to the original fish, which is actually their grandparent, the characteristic will become fairly well established in the strain.

When initial breeding stock has been obtained in this way the breeder can then proceed to concentrate on developing the freak condition into a fixed, altered characteristic and also, of course, concentrate on removing any undesirable side effects such as small size or poor health. Development of the new strain to a pure state may take many generations of careful and exacting work, but finally the aquarist may reach a point where all of the fish bred show the altered characteristic. At this point the strain can be tested for purity by flock breeding and if this proves successful the strain can be considered pure.

There are many complications to overcome in some particular cases but others may be exceptionally easy. It all depends on the nature of the required alteration. Some characteristics may be sex-linked, ie the hereditary factor may be carried only by the male or female fish but never both, or the characteristic may become so entangled with some other undesirable factor, perhaps a result of the particular inbreeding methods used, that it may become impossible or extremely difficult to continue the strain at all. All these problems are a challenge to the aquarist and this is of course what makes the cultivation of a new strain so interesting.

Breeding Techniques

Many of our common fish will breed quite easily without any help at all if their age and the environmental conditions are correct. This is indeed the reason why some species are so common and obviously the ease with which a species can be reproduced is a major factor in determining its price and availability in commercial aquatic establishments. The serious breeder should, however, take a certain amount of trouble, even with the easiest species, otherwise stunted and unhealthy fish may be produced or the young (or eggs) may be eaten at birth.

Fish which breed in a community aquarium will hardly ever

be successful because the young or spawn will be eaten. Some young livebearers may survive if they can shelter quickly after birth. Also, egglayer fry which are protected by their parents may survive if the demands on the parents are not too great during the protection period and if they are large enough at the end of this period to survive on their own; but these possibilities cannot be depended on. It is far better for the aquarist to provide proper breeding facilities and to carry out the exercise thoroughly.

During the earlier discussion of environmental conditions in Chapter 1, use was made of the springtime-summertime analogy and it was shown that definite conditions may be required by the fish to induce them to reproduce in captivity. The selected breeding stock must therefore be kept in environments where these conditions exist. For instance, most shoaling egglayers will come into readiness if the water temperature is increased to 80°F (27°C) and richer foods are given. These are not necessarily the conditions in which the species will actually breed but rather those which bring the prospective parents into good breeding condition. Some fish, such as the livebearers and the protective egglayers, can be conditioned and bred in the same environment and there is little point in any other method, but the majority of the common egglayers, which do not protect their eggs, will need more careful handling both to protect the eggs from the parents' appetites and from fungal growths. It will also be necessary to ensure that the female has enough eggs ready to produce a good batch of young.

Livebearers
These very common and popular fish are among the easiest to breed because they bear their young alive and fully formed. Most aquarists start breeding with livebearers, and for young aquarists especially the lessons learned and the experience gained are invaluable. Almost all our common livebearers (guppies, platies, mollies and swordtails) are so easy to breed that fry are produced regularly without any special involvement on the part of the aquarist. Unfortunately, as a result of careless breeding by inexperienced aquarists, this proclivity has led to a

weakening of some strains of these species over the years. At present there seems to be a shortage of really good livebearers and those generally available are often smaller, less hardy or not as representative of their species as they ought to be. The situation today is such that it is very difficult for an aquarist to acquire top-class unspoilt breeding stock in any particular strain. On the other hand, because of the ease of reproduction of these fish and the numbers of generations which can be produced in a remarkably short time, all of the common livebearers found in aquaria are now definite cultivated strains. This situation has been brought about by deliberate action by skilled breeders who have given us the wonderful colours and fin extensions now available in many of these fish.

Livebearers intended as parents are best kept away from egglaying fish and other livebearers of greatly differing size, otherwise bullying and fin-biting may occur. They are generally more vegetarian than most egglayers, so planted aquaria with soft algal growths are ideal. The young are born in cycles of about four weeks and the females are usually permanently pregnant from a very early age until old age. Even if the males are removed the females have an unusual ability to store sperm so that several subsequent broods can be produced from one mating. The males seem to be continuously sexually active when in good health so it is better to have at least twice as many females present as males (except where very strict selective breeding is practised, of course) so as to give individual females some chance of avoiding the constant attentions of the males. Certainly one female should never be kept with a group of males as this must impose a considerable strain.

It must also be remembered that it is possible for some livebearing species to interbreed, for instance platies x swordtails, so they should be kept separate. Furthermore, the water in environments containing male fish often contain live sperm which might easily be transferred to other environments, so some care is required with general cleanliness when working with a number of aquaria.

As a breeding example, let us discuss a trio of platies — two females and one male — whose offspring are required to be representative of the parents and the type generally but are not part of any complicated selective breeding system. The first requirement is that the adults should not be closely related as we are making the assumption that the strain is a fixed, although probably unnatural one, and there is thus no advantage in inbreeding. If the females are young and virgin then a period of growth separate from the male may be beneficial, but usually they will be pregnant when obtained and also holding stored sperm so a period for 'emptying out' may be advisable. Once a trio of mature adults with 'clean' females has been obtained they can then be put together in a suitable environment. Fry will be produced regularly and will not usually all be eaten at birth if the adults are properly fed. The newborn fry do not have complete control of their movement for a short period after birth and this is when they are most easily caught and eaten by adults. If they survive this period they then need cover of some kind and usually spend their first few days among surface vegetation, so the environment should be shallow and contain floating plants or other surface cover.

The young are born without any appreciable yolk-sac and feed almost immediately. Most livebearers can accept baby Brine Shrimp at once but will still benefit from Infusoria if given. Whatever the food used there must be plenty available so that the fish can feed at any time and in fact continuously if they wish. The first days are very important and any potential growth lost here is difficult to recover later.

Most female livebearers have anything between 20 and 200 young at a time, depending on their age and size, but an average of about 40 is reasonable. They can be left in the environment where they were born for about two weeks, with or without parents, but eventually must be moved to more spacious quarters for successful development. Some aquarists move the young to other quarters as soon as they are born and there is some argument as to which method is best, but certainly they must be moved some time during their early development, otherwise they will become stunted through lack of space in the original container, unless this is unusually large. The cause of this concern over the moving of the fry is that the operation may temporarily put them off their food and thus slow their rate of growth. If we also consider that newborn fry are probably more susceptible to damage by netting and handling, it might be thought better to leave the resettlement until as late as possible. There is also the fact that heavy feeding with fine foods during the first couple of weeks after birth might foul the original environment and this can be cleaned out for use again if the fish are moved after this period.

The larger, rearing container must of course reproduce the environment conditions which existed in the previous one, so that the move imposes as little shock to the fry as possible. Again heavy feeding will be needed so some thought must be given to the type of environment used. If some green food, such as garden peas, can be included in the diet as a substitute for natural plant and algal growth, a biological system can be utilised with consequent advantages from its large nitrifying potential. It is usual for experienced aquarists to rear about 100 fry to the young adult stage in a 20-gallon (90-litre) aquarium, but individual skill and technique may increase this figure surprisingly.

If the parent trio have been left in the original environment they will of course be producing more young even perhaps before the first batch has been moved out. This presents some difficulty for those aquarists operating on a limited scale and in these cases it may be better to use only one female and to remove the male elsewhere after mating. As mentioned before, it is pointless to breed more fish than can be reared to the adult stage satisfactorily, if only because the overcrowding which results will be to the disadvantage of all the young produced. (Methods and recommendations for the production of young fish in commercial quantities are discussed on pages 142–7.) Female livebearers are notoriously adverse to being moved about from one environment to another while pregnant. They are similarly harmed by enclosure in small containers such as breeding traps and jars. Female mollies in particular are extremely sensitive and often do not give birth at all if disturbed during pregnancy. They appear to absorb the young internally, or in some cases all may be stillborn.

Shoaling egglayers

Egglaying fish can be divided for breeding purposes into two types: those which protect and care for their eggs and young, and those which do not. The latter can be labelled for convenience as shoaling egglayers because most fish of this category live, and breed, in shoals in the natural state.

The shoaling egglayers include a great many of the popular aquarium fish such as the barbs, danios and tetras. These species are generally all representative of their wild counterparts and so inbreeding should not be encouraged. They are also suited to commercial quantity-production methods and hardly any of them have been altered by selective breeding. The behavioural intelligence of these fish is low and their breeding seems to be particularly dependent on instinctive actions triggered by environmental conditions, such as higher temperature and increased light intensity. Their eggs are simply scattered about during mating and may fall to the bottom or may adhere to plants in the vicinity. That is all the protection they receive and so they are a popular food with other fish and the parents themselves. To compensate for this the eggs are laid in hundreds and often thousands at a time. This creates a peculiar situation for the aquarist who wishes to breed these fish. Environmental triggers must be provided to induce the parents to spawn, the eggs must be guarded from the parents and other natural enemies including bacteria (intense light is also harmful to the eggs), and the resulting fry must be properly fed and then, when all this has been done, there will possibly be so many young fish that it will be difficult to raise them all satisfactorily. This kind of fish breeding is easily the most demanding because the aquarist gets no help from the fish themselves and is hindered by their presence once the actual spawning is finished, but it can also be extremely rewarding especially when one of the more difficult species has been bred successfully.

The main difficulty in breeding all egglayers is encountered during the period of two to five days when the eggs are hatching. At this time they are extremely prone to attack by fungus and once this is established the eggs affected are invariably lost and the fungus may spread to the others as well. Protective fish clean their eggs to prevent fungal attack but in other species the responsibility for protection is the aquarist's, and this task is very important. After the eggs have hatched the fry are still not fish in the true sense as they have an attached yolk-sac which they absorb before becoming free-swimming. During this time they do not feed and cannot swim about, but are relatively safe if properly looked after. The hatching period is definitely crucial and the aquarist must be prepared to devote all necessary attention to the eggs during this time.

Spawning environments required by various species vary but, in general, the common barbs and tetras spawn in clumps of fine plant or some substitute, while danios spawn over gravel or pebble beds. The barbs and tetras will be discussed together as an example of a typical situation and the danios will be considered later.

The normal mating procedure for a pair of typical plant-spawners is that the male fertilises the female's eggs while in very close contact with her and while lying in or pushing through a dense clump of fine plant. The spawning is preceded by chasing, butting and bumping and demonstrations of fin-spreading and colour intensity changes and other courtship displays. The spawning is usually followed by an avid egg-hunt unless the pair are removed promptly.

The spawning environment for these fish should consist of a small aquarium of about 10 gallons (45 litres) capacity which has previously been thoroughly cleaned internally. Everything used must be scrupulously clean to impede fungal attack of the eggs and nothing should be included which is not essential. Nylon knitting wool can be tangled into loose clumps as a substitute for plants and should be sterilised by boiling. The outside of the bottom glass of the aquarium can be painted so that gravel is not required (fish are unsettled over a transparent base) and a properly fitting cover glass to exclude dust and other atmospheric influences can be used. Water conditions (usually soft and acid), temperature, light and other factors should be set up for the species concerned and the water allowed to age for a little time. The breeding pair, which will have been conditioned separately elsewhere, can then be introduced in the evening and will usually spawn the next morning if all conditions are satisfactory. Sometimes a pair will not spawn until later in the day, or even the day after and when these delays are met the danger of fungal attack is increased. The fish should be made to jump or be dropped from the net into the water on introduction into the spawning environment so as to transfer as little as possible of the water and other constituents of the conditioning environment. If carried out sensibly, healthy fish will not be at all affected by this treatment and it is preferable for hygenic reasons to the alternative of dipping a possibly contaminated net in the water.

After spawning the pair must be removed as soon as possible. The net used for this purpose should be spotlessly clean and the operation must be carried out quickly and efficiently without disturbing the eggs more than is necessary. The aquarium should then be covered completely to exclude all light, and fungus preventative can be added at this stage. This is usually a 5 per cent aqueous solution of methylene blue, administered at two drops to the gallon, but one of the commercial substitutes can be used. There is now nothing for the aquarist to do for the time being unless the eggs show signs of fungus. Any affected eggs should be removed without creating a major disturbance, if this can be done, but no attempt should be made to touch or move healthy eggs as any bruising will encourage the growth of fungus. The crucial hatching period can, within limits, be shortened by increasing the temperature, so there is some advantage in keeping this as high as the eggs will tolerate.

Danios and other similar fish pose the same problems in somewhat different ways. These fish spawn while travelling together at some speed over a gravel bed. The eggs are not adhesive and simply fall to the bottom. The main problem encountered is that the fish often do not wait to finish spawning before eating their eggs. They will usually eat any eggs with which they come into contact while swimming about and due to their speed and mobility they often meet the eggs before they have reached the bottom. This means that some trouble must be taken to save the eggs if a reasonable yield is to be obtained. The popular method is to provide a long shallow container so that the fish are encouraged to swim up and down in more or less straight lines in the hope that by the time they are on their way back the eggs previously released will have reached the comparative safety of the gravel bed. Another method is to substitute a double layer of smooth round pebbles or glass marbles for the gravel so that the eggs fall between them to safety. The same recommendations for the cleanliness of the spawning environments apply here.

Selection and conditioning of breeding stock is usually carried out in groups and the fish are best spawned together in ratios of three or four males to two females. The reason for this is that the eggs are released by the female in full flight and the presence of a large number of males helps to ensure that all the eggs are fertilised satisfactorily. There is not a great deal of pre-spawning activity and not so much body contact as with the barbs and tetras, although there is often some butting and bumping. If the pebble method described above is utilised there is no great urgency to remove the adult fish immediately after spawning ends as the eggs should by then be quite safe. This can be an advantage as fish of this type will often spawn again after a short rest period, particularly if the females are in really good condition.

One point which requires special attention is that the fry of most shoaling egglayers kept in aquaria are so small that they initially require extremely fine foods. Some aquarists make do with the yolk from hard-boiled eggs or similar fine dry foods but for best results Infusoria must be used.

Protective egglayers
Cichlids and gouramies are examples of protective egglayers of which one or both of the parents always cares for the eggs through the difficult hatching period and then brings up the fry to the stage where they are reasonably capable of fending for themselves. By and large this behaviour of the parents is advantageous to the aquarist, although it does not make the process by any means easy. Most of these fish are more 'intelligent' and more individualistic than the shoaling types and often show themselves to be quite discriminating with respect to their

choice of spawning partner and their required environmental conditions. They will not often tolerate interference from the aquarist in the breeding process or from any other inhabitants of the environment.

One point which is sometimes not understood is that these fish are protective of their eggs or young only up to certain limits. It must never be thought that because they have produced viable spawn, success is ensured. If the environmental conditions are not right for the growth of the young, or if they are in great danger, they will be promptly eaten by their parents. Both of these factors are under the direct control of the aquarist who must therefore make every effort to help the parents in these matters, particularly by not allowing them to be frightened by unfamiliar human activities. In addition, when the fry have reached a certain size, a time comes when in the wild state they would naturally leave the parents to live their own lives. At this point the parental urge disappears and the parents see the young as just small fish, in other words as potential food. The aquarist must therefore split the family before this happens. Similarly, where only one parent guards the fry, the other fish, which in the wild would go away, must be removed after spawning as it will now be considered a potential danger to the fry by the guarding parent and may be killed or at least bullied.

Given the above limitations, most of these fish make excellent parents and some of the aquarist's happiest times will be spent watching them carry out their parental duties. The means used by the fish to overcome the tendency of the eggs to be attacked by fungus are varied in the extreme and some methods, such as bubble-nesting and mouth-breeding, are so fantastic as to be unbelievable to the novice, but whichever method is employed the results are the same and the recommendations for success are more or less similar. Many of these fish grow to a relatively large size by maturity and some are among the largest fish kept in aquaria, so their spawning environment may have to be somewhat larger than those used for other groups. Furthermore, because the young may stay with the parents for as long as six weeks before the urge to disperse appears, the environment may need to be set up in a more permanent fashion. Some essential differences in method must be made between those types which have complete parental care and those which involve only one parent. Most of the fish are natural strains and should be treated as such with regard to the selection of breeding stock, but there are some important exceptions, which are classic examples of cultivated strains, such as the Siamese Fighting Fish and the fancy angelfish.

The gouramies and other anabantids practise single-parent protection and also construct a bubble-nest just beneath the surface of the water. Since the male is usually the active partner, there is some considerable danger to the female in the confines of the aquarium and the aquarist must be very careful of the way in which the inactive parent is employed. A male in full breeding condition will often tolerate the female's presence only during the actual courtship and spawning and may kill or harm her afterwards. Furthermore, if she is not in breeding condition or is not receptive to that particular male then she must be removed to prevent injury from his repeatedly frustrated attempts to breed. In the wild, of course, the female would either go away or be driven away from the vicinity of the male, but she cannot do this in a small aquarium.

The bubble-nest is usually built by the male, who requires a clean water surface free of draughts and dust. The preliminary courtship is often involved and long-winded but extremely interesting. Spawning takes place beneath the nest and the female is usually driven away afterwards. She can be carefully removed at this point but this must be done without breaking up or disturbing the bubble-nest. If left alone and not threatened the male will generally hatch the eggs and care for the young satisfactorily. He will become aggressive towards any interference by the aquarist and may not feed much during this period. The spawning environment need only be normally clean and not virtually sterile as for shoaling egglayers as the guarding fish will continually clean the eggs to keep fungus at bay. The one point of some importance is the condition of the water surface. This must be clean and the young fish must not be exposed to draughty conditions when using their labyrinth organs to take in atmospheric air. Some anabantid fry are extremely small and so must have Infusoria for their first food, while a few species are large enough to use brine shrimps immediately.

The cichlid family are the most apparently intelligent of all aquarium fish and usually exercise devoted parental care. Often both sexes take an equal part in raising the fry and frequently the two fish will mate for life and show no interest in other fish of the opposite sex. Many members of this group, for instance angelfish, do not show sexual characteristics until they reach maturity. They are therefore best raised together in a group of at least six so that breeding couples can pair off naturally. An established pair can then be separated from the rest and installed in a permanent environment in which they can breed and raise their young without disturbance. There are many patterns of spawning behaviour, all of which involve different ways of protecting the eggs and young against fungus and other enemies. Some cichlids use caves, or flower pots if provided, some dig pits in the gravel bed, some spawn on plant leaves or the sides of the aquarium and, of course, the mouth-breeders have their own characteristic methods.

The cichlids are generally very easy to breed if their needs are understood. The parent fish must be truly adult and well fed at all times with meaty foods, preferably earthworms, as most of them are naturally carnivorous. They will not tolerate other inhabitants in the spawning environment and many will not even tolerate plants. Environmental conditions must be adjusted to their liking and if seriously frightened they will eat the eggs or fry. The parents usually take turns to care for and clean their offspring and during this time the other parent will often take up a guarding posture at a fixed distance, presumably as a front-line defence against natural enemies.

The most interesting part of the exercise for the aquarist comes after the fry are free-swimming. Up to this time the parents' jobs are fairly straightforward and in the artificial environment are mainly concerned with cleanliness; but once the fry start to swim properly they have a tendency to wander and a lot of time is then spent in catching strays and generally keeping the fry in a tight shoal. Relationships between the parents during this time are almost always good and there is a fair division of labour and responsibility. Finally of course, the dispersion point is reached and then the young must be removed if they are not to be eaten, although with some cichlids this may not occur if the parents are kept well fed. The young should still be removed, however, if overcrowding is likely, and in any event, should the parents spawn again, the original fry would be a serious nuisance. Spawnings generally produce about 400 fry and the young are quite large at hatching and grow quickly if properly fed. They need meaty foods such as boiled, crumbled liver and also thrive on small Daphnia, newly-hatched Brine Shrimp and chopped Whiteworm.

Other egglayers
There are, of course, many egglaying fish kept in aquaria other than those groups mentioned above. Some of these breed in a somewhat similar fashion, while others breed in widely different ways. A great many common fish have never been bred at all in aquaria and others which have produced young have not yet been observed during the actual spawning. All this makes for interest for the aquarist and leaves much experimental work to be done by the more seriously minded person.

The rules behind all fishbreeding are basically the same, however, and can be summarised as follows:

1 The chosen parents should be properly adult and in good breeding condition. They should not be related unless deliberate inbreeding is intended.
2 The conditioning process and the spawning environment must favour the species concerned in every possible way.
3 The hatching period of the eggs must be attended by the utmost care and attention to prevent fungal attack, except where the parents exercise complete protection.
4 Parents which eat eggs or young must be removed as soon as possible, or protective cover must be established.
5 Newborn fry must be provided with small-sized foods fre-

quently enough and in sufficient quantities to achieve their full growth-rate potential.

6 Growing fry must have space enough to prevent overcrowding, and other environmental conditions such as temperature must be correct.

7 Separation of the young from the parents must be carried out before the fish's instinctive dispersal time occurs.

Quantity Production

Many aquarists will eventually develop an interest in producing fish on an efficient commercial or semi-commercial basis. This is quite a feasible ambition, although the profitability of the enterprise will depend on the abilities of the individual. The breeding and raising techniques involved will be as described above but attention must also be focused on the quantity and regularity of production of sizeable batches of young fish.

To take a hypothetical situation as an example, suppose an aquarist wishes to have available for sale every week 100 fish of reasonable size of one of the easily-spawned species of shoaling egglayers. The first consideration is the volume of water required to cater for such a quantity. The three stages involved in the breeding programme are conditioning, spawning and development, and there must be available aquaria in which to carry out all of these. During conditioning, small to medium-sized adult fish can be accommodated in two aquaria, one for males and the other for females. Two 15-gal (68-litre) aquaria will be suitable. The number of adults required to ensure weekly spawnings, and to allow a spare well-conditioned pair, is about four pairs, but six is better and gives the fish more of a rest between spawnings and plenty of chance to get into good condition again.

The spawning aquarium should have a capacity from 5–10 gallons (22–45 litres) depending on the species, but should not be larger than necessary if problems of hygiene are to be avoided. The young fry will usually live in these environments for at least the first two weeks after spawning, so a minimum number of three spawning aquaria will be required for weekly rotation. The rearing aquaria can have a capacity of 20 gallons (90 litres) or more so that at least 100 fry can be accommodated in each. Assuming that a good aquarist can rear the fry to a reasonable 'selling size' in, say, ten weeks, then eight of these rearing aquaria at least would be required after allowing for the first two weeks in the spawning aquaria.

This brings the minimum total to three small, two medium and eight large aquaria, if each spawning produces about 100 fry. If more are produced then further rearing aquaria can be utilised, and if less are produced then further spawning environments can be set up and additional breeding pairs used so that the system can be run at full capacity. Such a system will use not less than 200 gallons (900 litres) of water and on average at any one time there will be about 1,000 fish to look after. Electrical power consumption to provide normal tropical temperatures will be around 1kW if all the thermostats switch on at the same time, and a fair amount of pumped air will be needed to supply all the various appliances.

It can therefore be seen that fish production in even reasonable quantities is not an easy matter and requires quite complex set-ups. One hundred fish produced per week may seem a lot at first, but this will not produce any appreciable income, after expenses, unless the species concerned is some valuable variety. A target of 500 or more fish per week would seem reasonable to provide a worthwhile income and it can be seen just what would be involved in attaining this figure. In spite of all this complexity, however, many aquarists do breed fish in saleable quantities, if only to pay for the upkeep of other non-productive fish, and these home-bred fish are usually healthier, larger and better coloured than their imported counterparts and can be purchased with confidence. Breeders disposing of home-produced fish in large quantities will usually be doing so through a commercial wholesaler or retailer and must realise that they can expect to be paid at most 50 per cent of whatever price the fish will finally fetch. Their economics must be based on this figure and not on the shopkeeper's selling price.

The daily food requirements of several hundred young fish are quite substantial and this is the point on which many would-be quantity producers fail. The fry must be fed properly and often, which can be costly and time-consuming. Two or three feeds a day are not really enough, so the amateur aquarist who is away at work will probably depend on other members of the family for help. If he buys commercial fish foods at today's retail prices it is unlikely that he will ever cover his costs. Luckily many of the better foods such as Infusoria and Whiteworm can readily be cultured after some practice, and Brine Shrimp eggs for hatching can be bought in bulk at reasonable prices. Daphnia can be collected in most localities and earthworms obtained from the garden. Commercial dry flake and powder foods can be ignored and dry cat and dog foods used in their place. Inevitably, the difficulties of consistently obtaining large quantities of any of the above foods will ensure that a varied diet is provided, and this is good for the fish. Cooked peas, liver and fish roe and other table foods should also be used.

From time to time all aquarists will encounter epidemics of white spot, velvet or other contagious diseases. The aquarist with hundreds of fish must be on guard at all times to avoid disease and the resulting complications in breeding schedules, which may be very severe. Each aquarium should have its own thermometer. The common practice of having only one or two thermometers and moving these about as needed does not encourage frequent temperature checks. Similarly, it is better if each aquarium has its own thermostat. Nets, scrapers and other accessories should be cleaned between immersions in different aquaria and there is a good argument for each aquarium having its own tool-kit. When a disease does strike every possible precaution must be taken immediately and priority must be given to eliminating the trouble. Most common diseases can be cured nowadays with the appropriate proprietary products if the treatment is started soon enough, so a stock of these medicines should be kept. Sick or convalescing fish should not be sold until they are completely recovered and have gone through a proving period of at least a month. Some spare aquarium capacity is advisable for this purpose.

Inevitably, those who keep numerous fish are likely to have to kill very sick, injured or badly deformed specimens from time to time and a method should be developed to do this as humanely as possible. Mistakes during inbreeding may produce deformities such as the hump-backed guppies often seen and while these should not be produced if breeding stock is properly selected, nothing is perfect. The kindest way to kill small fish is probably to feed them quickly to some larger hungry fish which will immediately swallow them whole. Sick fish which cannot be disposed of in this way should be dropped into boiling water. They should not be allowed to swim about in a frightened state with a fish which may or may not eat them, and nor should they be fed to a fish which will bite or tear them before death occurs. The practice of flushing unwanted fish down the toilet is cruel as they may not die for a long while. Strains of breeding stock which produce unhealthy or deformed fish should not be used again and no species should be bred unless the correct environment and foods are available; poor conditions will encourage the accumulation of imperfect fish.

It will be found that in the rearing environments used in any quantity breeding system some compromise must be reached between ease of maintenance and convenience of feeding. Theoretically the biological system should be the answer, there being no decorative requirements and no need for plant growth, but it may be found that even a good biological system may not cope with pollutants if the fish are fed only infrequently and hence with rather large quantities at one time, or if the environment is on the point of being overcrowded. In these cases it will probably be necessary to organise a programme of water-changing to ensure regular dilution of toxic substances and urine. Some foods such as whiteworm may be lost in gravel beds when fed in quantity so some thought must also be given to this problem. A further point is that when young fish find themselves crowded together in a small volume of water they exude biological substances (pheromones) into the water which inhibit the development of the weaker members of the shoal, presumably for reasons of natural selection. It is assumed that only water-changing can combat the effects of this situation, although the use of adsorbent filter materials might prove effective.

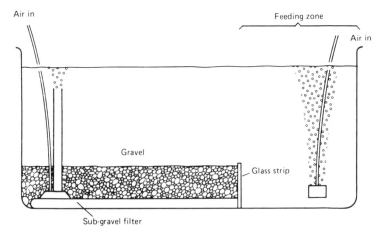

Fig 41 A simple method of feeding in which an area free from gravel is used. This area can easily be kept clean

A useful idea for making it easier to keep environments clean is shown in Figure 41. The aquarium is provided with a bare area on which all sinking food is placed, thus making it very easy to remove uneaten remains. Meanwhile the gravel bed section of the base will be functioning as a normal biological system and when mature will still have sufficient nitrifying potential to justify its inclusion. This method works well in practice and it is found that a change of about one bucket of water weekly in a 20-gallon (90-litre) aquarium gives good results. An airstone can be added at the bare end and the ascending column of bubbles will produce the protein skimmer cleansing action described on page 53. It will be found that the fish find the food quickly on the bare base area and that foods such as whiteworm which live for some little time after submergence can be fed in largish quantities without worry.

When protective egglayers are bred for quantity it is a common practice to remove the eggs from the parents as soon as possible. This does not seem to worry the parents overmuch and they will often spawn again after a few days if they are in condition. If possible, removal of the eggs should be done without exposing them to the air and they should not be handled directly but should be removed on the leaf or stone on which they were laid, or siphoned off through a wide pipe if loose in a pit.

Anabantid eggs can be sucked into a wide-necked jar complete with bubble-nest. Eggs laid on the container walls or on very large rocks cannot be moved successfully and so must be left to the parents. The eggs should be placed in a small, dark, sterile environment with medication against fungus and aeration to stimulate water movement around them. They are then treated in the same way as the eggs of the shoaling egglayers. Exceptions to this are the Discus fish, whose young must feed initially on the mucus from the bodies of their parents and do not often survive without it, and the mouth-breeders, whose eggs will most likely be unobtainable. By removing the eggs in this way it is possible to produce numerous frequent spawnings from one good pair of adults, although it would seem that this must eventually impose some unnatural strain on their bodies. A pair of Angelfish, for instance, have been known to spawn every week for eighteen months.

Some fish, such as the white cloud mountain minnows and corydoras catfish, take no notice of their eggs after spawning if properly fed and can be quite safely left with them. This fact lends itself to a very simple method. A large natural system, suited to the specific needs of the fish, is set up, the breeding stock is installed, and from time to time batches of young can be removed. Snails, which are avid egg-eaters, must be completely excluded along with any other harmful creatures, and the approximate population of the environment must be known at all times so that the correct amount and variety of foods can be given, but otherwise the system is very easy to administer. Fish which are easily bred in this way can be used to fill in gaps in other rearing schedules or can simply be held back in their own aquarium when others are plentiful.

8
Tests and Measurements

There are various methods available to the average aquarist for testing the conditions in an artificial environment. It is not intended to give the impression that all of these measurements are essential to the well-being of the environment but rather to bring them to the aquarist's notice and to recommend suitable ways of carrying them out. Certain measurements, eg temperature and density, are of course essential in some types of environment, but most of the others are either precautionary or are used at the discretion of the aquarist when trouble of some kind is encountered. There is much to be said for not taking too many unnecessary measurements on a continuous basis as this complicates fishkeeping considerably and may lead to concern when in fact there is nothing wrong at all.

Temperature

There is nothing to be gained by using any instrument other than a thermometer as it is so simple to use and quite accurate enough for aquarium use. Aquarium temperatures are usually measured in °F; for the conversion equation to obtain °C see page 68. Thermometers should be left on view in the aquarium so that readings can be quickly taken at any time.

Density

The density of the water in a salt environment is used as a measure of the salinity of the water. In the case of marine environments the prepacked salts available are prepared so that they can be mixed with fresh water until a certain density reading is obtained, at which point the optimum type of salt water will have been created. The term 'density' may also be referred to as

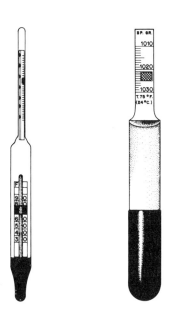

Fig 42 A combined thermometer-hydrometer (left) and an all-plastic hydro-meter *(Courtesy Interpret Ltd)*. The hydrometer must float unimpeded in static water and for accuracy should be calibrated for the correct water temperature

'specific gravity' or 'relative density' in various publications but they all mean the same thing as far as the aquarist is concerned.

Density is measured with the use of a hydrometer (Figure 42). This is a small glass device, rather like a thermometer in appearance, which is floated upright in the aquarium water. It contains internal ballast weight and a calibrated scale, and will float either higher or lower in the water depending on the density. The correct density measurement is obtained by noting where the water surface line intersects the internal calibrated scale and a reliable reading can be taken only in static water. Since the density of water changes with temperature, hydro-meters are supplied already calibrated for use at a given temper-ature. However, a difference of, say, 5°F (3°C) between the required and actual temperatures produces only a negligible error. The usual hydrometers supplied to aquarists are calib-rated either at 60°F (15.5°C) for coldwater environments or 75°F (24°C) for tropical use. The use of a 60°F (15.5°C) hydro-meter in a tropical environment will result in an incorrect read-ing of some significance.

The hydrometer can be left in the aquarium so that it is always available and easily referred to when needed. If for any reason this is not easily managed, as for instance in a decorative aquarium, a sample of the water may need to be taken and the hydrometer floated in this, preferably in a narrow container such as a jam jar or a tumbler.

Hydrogen Ion Concentration (pH)

The pH value of water is a measure of its acidity or alkalinity and refers to its hydrogen ion concentration. Pure water is used as a standard for calibration and has the pH value 7.0. Waters with a pH above 7.0 are called alkaline, whereas those with values below 7.0 are called acid. The simplest method of measuring pH employs chemically-treated litmus papers which are immersed in the water. The papers change to a certain colour which can then be compared with a standard colour scale to obtain the pH value. The resolution, ie the smallest difference which can be determined, is not very good but nevertheless the accuracy is usually adequate for aquarium purposes. Sources of error are in the interpretation of the colours by the user or through deterioration of the indicator paper or the colour chart supplied, for instance through prolonged exposure to sunlight.

A pH meter, which gives a direct reading on a calibrated scale, can also be used, although it is a somewhat expensive purchase. The device is straightforward and easy to use and is less prone to errors of individual interpretation. A probe is simply immersed in the water sample for a short period and the pH value is read off from the scale. The instrument is recommended to serious aquarists in preference to the paper method.

Chemical or biological additions, using commercially available pH adjusters or materials such as peat, may be made to the water to adjust the pH value to a desired figure, but much care and attention is required and such alterations are not recommended for casual reasons only. If water of the correct type for a certain project, such as breeding a particular species, cannot be obtained by any other means then some previous practice is recommended in an unpopulated volume of water, and fish or other animals should be included only when the aquarist is confident of his methods. When alterations to the pH value are made, measurements are of course necessary otherwise the conditions created will be unknown and may prove fatal to any inhabitants. Once alterations are successfully made, the conditions set up will need to be maintained.

Many of the items normally found in aquaria can have a gradual influence on the pH value if the water remains unchanged for a long period. Soft rocks and some gravels generally induce alkalinity through the slow release of mineral salts into the water; peat produces acidity; and many other similar effects may be encountered. The influence of photosynthesis on pH (see page 18) should be borne in mind. Bacteria are affected by the pH value of the water. Very acid waters are generally free of bacteria and, although this may be advantageous when breeding some fish, it should be remembered that biological filters depend on bacterial action and very acid waters do not therefore encourage a high nitrifying potential.

In marine environments the range of pH values encountered is generally more restricted than those found in freshwater. Values from 7.9 to 8.4 cover most requirements and most marine life must be kept within these limits. Some paper indicators and measuring kits designed for freshwater use are not accurate in salt water and enquiries should be made before they are purchased for marine use. The relatively high expense of complex marine environments may justify the purchase of an electronic pH meter.

Calcium Carbonate Content

The measurement of the calcium carbonate content of a water sample provides a measure of its degree of 'hardness' or 'softness'. The numbers used are in units of parts per million (ppm). Thus 50 ppm means 50 parts of calcium carbonate dissolved in a million parts of water. Other units may, however, be used and details of these are given in Table 10. The relevant information for tap-water supplies can be obtained from area water authorities or specific measurements can be taken by chemical

TABLE 10 CONVERSION OF WATER HARDNESS SCALES

English	1°Clark	=	14.3ppm (1 grain/gallon)	CaCo3
German	1°DH	=	17.8ppm (1 = 100,000)	CaCo3
American	1°	=	1ppm	CaCo3

Conversions	°Clark x 0.8	=	°DH
	°DH x 1.24	=	°Clark
	°Clark x 14.3	=	ppm CaCo3

or electronic means. However, these measurements are rarely essential. There are two types of hardness, known as 'temporary' and 'permanent'. Temporary hardness is removed by boiling the water, while permanent hardness is unaffected by this operation. Table 11 gives an indication of the numerical hardness values of various categories of water.

TABLE 11 CATEGORIES OF WATER

Hardness (ppm)	Category
50	Soft
100	Medium soft
150	Slightly hard
250	Medium hard
350	Hard

Chemical means of hardness testing of reliable accuracy are generally beyond the means of the average aquarist and involve fairly complex soap tests in which the ability of the water to lather a standard soap solution is used as a measure of the hardness. Simple kits are, however, available which give a rougher indication of hardness. An electronic meter, similar to the pH meter mentioned above, is also available but is rather expensive. The meter will give good reliable readings and its accuracy and resolution are more than adequate.

Hardness and pH values are closely tied together in natural and tap-waters, so alterations to one invariably affect the other. Water may be softened by being passed through a resin which absorbs mineral substances and can be hardened by the addition of materials (eg rocks and gravels) containing calcium carbonate which is then slowly released into the water. Generally, in fishkeeping, the impression is given that most plants, fish and other animals benefit from soft water. This information is sound on a broad basis only as it must always be remembered that there are creatures which depend on hard water for a healthy existence. Shelled creatures, for instance, require hard water for good shell formation and some plants are surprisingly dependent on it.

Domestic water-softening machines are not suitable for aquarium use, as they generate additives which are not compatible with the aquarium's biological requirements.

Oxygen and Carbon Dioxide Content

The oxygen-carbon dioxide relationship is one of the most fundamental and important factors in the aquarium (see page 18). Unfortunately, it is difficult for the average person to perform any kind of reliable measurement without chemical knowledge and apparatus; but because of the importance of this factor experienced aquarists have long since learned how to judge the condition of their aquaria in this respect. The fish themselves are the best available indicators of oxygen deficiency and/or carbon dioxide excess. The danger signs are lassitude, bad health, lack of interest in food and other similar characteristics. Bad cases are shown by fish attempting to breathe atmospheric oxygen from the air at the water surface. This condition can be adequately cured or avoided by good hygiene, sufficient water surface area and strong artificial aeration. Even though this environmental factor cannot easily be measured, empirically it can be taken care of satisfactorily by common sense and the conscientious aquarist should never feel the need for a definite measurement.

Whilst on the subject of oxygen-carbon dioxide exchanges, it is worth mentioning that every organism living in water is surrounded by an 'envelope' of stationary water which acts as an interface between its body and the surrounding environment. The thickness of this layer will determine the rate and efficiency with which the organism can exchange gases and other diffusible materials with that environment, and is apparently determined by the amount of water movement present in the environment and the normal mobility of the organism. Static organisms are, of course, totally dependent on water movement to reduce the effect of this stationary layer. A slow or fixed creature, such as a sea anemone which normally lives in a very turbulent environment and hence has only a thin envelope in nature, will suffer in a quiet, still aquarium by being surrounded by a layer of stationary water which is thicker than its body mechanisms can normally deal with; its exchange processes will take place at a slower and less efficient rate than its normal requirement. This may be one of the reasons why some creatures of this type never settle in one place in the aquarium but wander about unnaturally as though seeking better conditions. Off-colour fish will often be seen to dart about abnormally and again it may be that they obtain temporary relief from this condition by increased activity. Although an environment may be sufficiently oxygenated generally, it may still be unsatisfactory for certain inhabitants because of the lack of enough movement or turbulence to reduce the thickness of their individual envelopes to enable proper exchanges to take place.

Finally, it should be noted that salt water holds less oxygen in solution than does fresh water at the same temperature. This is a result of the higher chemical content of salt water which effectively leaves 'less room' available for the dissolved gases. Furthermore, the ability of any given solution to hold dissolved oxygen decreases as its temperature increases.

Nitrite Content

Some indication of the efficiency with which the nitrogen cycle is being completed can be best obtained by measuring the content of ammonia, nitrate or nitrite present at a given time (see page 46). The toxicity to fish of these three constituents of the nitrogen cycle, in order of severity, is typically as follows:

	mg per litre
Ammonia	0.5
Nitrite	15
Nitrate	150

Although ammonia is obviously the worst enemy, nitrite is not far behind and its concentration is an extremely useful indicator, which can be measured by a simple and reliable method. If the nitrite concentration is zero or very low the aquarist can be sure that the nitrogen cycle is being completed satisfactorily.

This nitrite measurement is accomplished by means of a simple procedure in which a standard chemical solution is added to a sample of water and the resulting colour change is noted, and compared with a standard colour scale. The method is most useful for testing the efficiency of biological filtration systems and, in particular, for determining when these systems are fully matured. Mainly as a result of the commercial pressures of the marine side of fishkeeping, salt-water nitrite test kits have been developed which are extremely accurate and have high resolution.

Kits are also available which determine the nitrate and ammonia contents but, in view of the interrelationships of the three substances in the nitrogen cycle, there is no general necessity for testing for all three and so the established nitrite method remains satisfactory for practical purposes.

Appendix

The Electrical Appliances (Safety) Regulations 1975

These Regulations, which became effective in the UK during 1976, are relevant to the manufacture of all electrical appliances, including pumps, heaters, thermostats and any other electrical equipment for the aquarist. Although they apply only to the manufacture of new equipment, and the aquarist can therefore continue to use older existing equipment, it is recommended that existing installations are checked for safety against these official standards. Those with a responsibility for public safety (schools, hospitals etc) may wish to modify their installations to meet the Regulations.

The relevant sections are:

Regulation 5

. . . parts not intended to be electrified . . . shall be separated from parts intended to be electrified . . . by sufficient additional or supplementary insulation . . . to ensure protection against an electric shock in the event of failure of the basic insulation . . .

This Regulation clearly implies that all live components in a piece of equipment should be doubly insulated where the primary insulation or covering is breakable. Unfortunately, double insulation does not go hand-in-hand with efficient heat transfer from heating elements or with good temperature sensitivity in thermostats.

Regulation 6

. . . where any part of an appliance to which these Regulations apply which is intended to be electrified is capable of causing an electric shock to a person touching it, the appliance shall be so designed that that part is not capable of being touched by a hand or with a finger, without something first being done to the appliance which requires the use of tools.

This is only common sense. From the aquarist's point of view it means that several potentially dangerous constructions of equipment have now been modified by the manufacturers. These include thermostats which could be removed from their glass tubes by the simple extraction of a rubber bung, air pumps which have pull-off bases and thus expose live terminals, and aquarium cable connectors made with snap-on covers. All covers and access points now have to be designed so that they can be reached only by removing retaining screws or similar fixings.

Bibliography

Aquarists who are only concerned with one branch of fishkeeping, for instance freshwater tropicals, should always be aware of the advantages in reading books concerned with other branches of the hobby. This applies particularly in the case of books written supposedly only for marine aquarists. The commercial pressures in this speciality have stimulated a great deal of research, with the result that books dealing with marine aquaria are full of information which is often equally applicable to freshwater fishkeeping.

Dal Vesco, Vanna et al. *Life in the Aquarium* (Octopus, 1975)
de Graaf, Frank. *Marine Aquarium Guide* (Pet Library, 1973)
Ghadially, Feroze N. *Advanced Aquarist Guide* (Pet Library, 1969)
Huckstedt, Guido. *Water Chemistry* (TFH Publications, 1973)
Kubler, Rolf. *Light in the Aquarium* (TFH Publications, 1973)
Matsui, Dr Yoshiichi. *Goldfish Guide* (Pet Library, 1972)
Muhlberg, Helmut. *The Complete Guide to Water Plants* (EP Publishing, 1982)
Nikolsky, G. V. *The Ecology of Fishes* (Academic Press, 1963)
Spotte, Stephen. *Marine Aquarium Keeping* (John Wiley and Sons, 1973)
Sterba, Gunther. *The Aquarist's Encyclopedia* (Blandford, 1983)
——— *Freshwater Fishes of the World* (Studio Vista, 1962)
van Duijn Jur, C. *Diseases of Fishes* (Illfe Books, 1956)
Van Ramshorst, Dr J. D. *The Complete Aquarium Encyclopedia* (Phaidon, 1978)

Acknowledgements

No one produces a book unaided, especially one concerned with such an involved hobby as aquarium keeping. All knowledge comes from one's own experience and that of others, and is gradually built up over a number of years, from reading about the subject as well as from being involved in it. I would therefore like to acknowledge my debts to the many other authors in this field, particularly those mentioned in the Bibliography, and those who over the years have contributed to the *Aquarist and Pondkeeper* and other periodicals.

I would also acknowledge the many conversations — arguments, even — with acquaintances, and general help received from my aquatic friends who have often been used as sounding boards for my theories and ideas, and those members of the aquatic equipment trade who have helped with illustrative material and information.

Finally, I must thank my family for putting up with me and my 'fishy' ways for so long.

A. J.
Highley, Shropshire

Index

Entries in **bold** type refer to main subject headings